THE CONSTRUCTION AND USE OF ECONOMIC MODELS

APPLIED MATHEMATICS SERIES

CONSULTING EDITORS

IAN N. SNEDDON, M.A. (Cantab.), D.Sc., F.R.S.E.
Simson Professor of Mathematics, University of Glasgow

F. M. ARSCOTT, M.Sc., Ph.D., F.I.M.A.
Professor of Mathematics, University of Surrey

GENERAL EDITOR

F. BOWMAN, M.A. (Cantab.), M.Sc.Tech.
Formerly Head of the Department of Mathematics, College of Science and Technology, Manchester

---

COMPUTER PROGRAMMING AND AUTOCODES
D. G. BURNETT-HALL, M.A.
L. A. G. DRESEL, M.A., Ph.D.
P. A. SAMET, B.Sc., Ph.D.

DIFFERENTIAL EQUATIONS
S. V. FAGG, B.Sc., A.R.C.S., D.I.C.

AN INTRODUCTION TO COMPUTATIONAL METHODS
K. A. REDISH, B.Sc.

VIA VECTOR TO TENSOR
W. G. BICKLEY, D.Sc., F.R.Ae.S., A.C.G.I.
R. E. GIBSON, Ph.D., A.C.G.I., A.M.I.C.E.

INTRODUCTION TO DETERMINANTS AND MATRICES
F. BOWMAN, M.A. (Cantab), M.Sc.Tech.

INTRODUCTION TO THE MATHEMATICS OF SERVOMECHANISMS
J. L. DOUCE, M.Sc., Ph.D., M.I.E.E.

HYDRODYNAMICS AND VECTOR FIELD THEORY
Volume One: Examples in Elementary Methods
Volume Two: Examples in Special Methods
D. M. GREIG, M.A. (Cantab.), M.Sc.(Lond.), Ph.D.
T. H. WISE, M.A. (Cantab.)

PREDICTION AND REGULATION
by Linear Least-Square Methods
P. WHITTLE, M.Sc.(N.Z.), Ph.D.(Uppsala)

INTRODUCTION TO ALGOL PROGRAMMING
R. WOOLDRIDGE, M.C., B.Sc.
J. F. RACTLIFFE, C.B.E., F.R.S.

THE CONSTRUCTION AND USE OF ECONOMIC MODELS

A. R. BERGSTROM, M.Com., Ph.D.
Professor of Econometrics,
University of Auckland,
New Zealand

THE ENGLISH UNIVERSITIES PRESS LTD
ST PAUL'S HOUSE WARWICK LANE
LONDON EC4

First printed 1967

Set in Times New Roman by the Monotype 4-line Mathematical system.
Printed in Great Britain for The English Universities Press Limited,
by Richard Clay (The Chaucer Press), Ltd., Bungay, Suffolk

PREFACE

ANY set of assumptions that approximately describes an economy or a sector of an economy can be called an economic model. Thus all economic theory is concerned with the formulation and analysis of models. But most of these models are too imprecise to be used as a basis for econometric work. During the last thirty years there has been great progress in the formulation and analysis of more precise models which are suitable for statistical fitting and can be used as a basis for the prediction and regulation of the behaviour of actual economies. Associated with this development there has been a greater emphasis on the rigorous deduction of the implications of economic models. And, during the same period, there have been important advances in the statistical methods of econometrics. The purpose of this book is to give a brief exposition and synthesis of these developments.

The reader is assumed to have a basic knowledge of pure mathematics and statistical theory. But no familiarity with economics is assumed.

The book was planned and commenced in 1964 when I was a Reader at the London School of Economics. It has been influenced by many stimulating discussions with my former colleagues there.

A. R. Bergstrom

Auckland

EDITORS' FOREWORD

THE object of this series is to provide texts in applied mathematics which will cover school and university requirements and extend to the post-graduate field. The texts will be convenient for use by pure and applied mathematicians and also by scientists and engineers wishing to acquire mathematical techniques to improve their knowledge of their own subjects. Applied mathematics is expanding at a great rate, and every year mathematical techniques are being applied in new fields of physical, biological, and economic sciences. The series will aim at keeping abreast of these developments. Wherever new applications of mathematics arise it is hoped to persuade a leader in the field to describe them briefly.

F. BOWMAN, M.A. (Cantab.), M.Sc.Tech.
Formerly Head of the Department of Mathematics,
College of Science and Technology, Manchester.

IAN N. SNEDDON, M.A. (Cantab.), D.Sc., F.R.S.E.
Simson Professor of Mathematics,
University of Glasgow.

F. M. ARSCOTT, M.Sc., Ph.D., F.I.M.A.
Professor of Mathematics,
University of Surrey.

CONTENTS

CHAPTER 1
INTRODUCTION

1.1 Types of Economic Model

ECONOMIC MODELS can be broadly classified into two types. The first type includes models that are designed to provide insight into the properties of actual or hypothetical economic systems, but whose parameters could not be estimated from empirical data. As examples we have those models in which the technology of an economy is described by the parameters of a large number of possible *activities*, most of which are never used (see, for example, von Neumann (1945)).

The second type includes models whose parameters could, conceivably, be estimated from empirical data, and which could be used as a basis for prediction or decision-making. Such models may provide valuable insight also. But this is not their sole purpose. They can be classified into three subtypes. The first includes models of the firm, which can be used as a basis for decision-making at the firm level. The second includes models of a centrally planned economy, which can be used as a basis for decision-making by the central planning authority. The third includes models of a decentralised economy or a sector of such an economy. Such models can be used either for forecasting or as a basis for regulation.

It is with models of the last subtype that this book is concerned. The models will, in most cases, require some modification before being applied to an actual economy. It may, for example, be necessary to incorporate particular features of a country's taxation system. But they have the basic features of various types of model that can be used in practical econometric work. They can be regarded, therefore, as prototype econometric models.

1.2 Continuous versus Discrete Models

One of the most important methodological questions relating to the construction of economic models is the question of whether it is better to formulate such models as systems of differential or difference equations. Although many individual economic decisions are made at regular intervals (for example, weekly or monthly), the variables that are observed by the econometrician are the outcome of a large number of decisions taken by different individuals at different points of time. Moreover, the intervals at which most economic variables are observed are larger than the intervals between the decisions that they reflect. These facts suggest that the variables that enter into a typical econometric model should be treated as continuous functions of time and that the model should be formulated as a system of differential equations.

Although many, if not most, of the models discussed in the theoretical literature are of the continuous sort, those used in applied econometric studies are usually formulated as systems of difference equations. This is, presumably, because of the practical difficulty of obtaining estimates of the parameters of systems of *stochastic differential equations* from discrete observations of the variables. But there is no reason in principle why such estimates should not be obtained. Moreover, the techniques that have been developed by econometricians for the estimation of the parameters of *discrete models* can be utilised in the estimation of the parameters of *continuous models* (see Bergstrom (1966) and Chapter 9, *infra*).

It could be argued that, since a set of equispaced observations generated by a system of linear stochastic differential equations satisfies a system of linear stochastic difference equations (see Chapter 9, *infra*), we should concentrate on the estimation of the parameters of the latter system. For this system is all that we require for the prediction of future observations. Suppose, for example, that the observations are generated by the system

$$Dy(t) = Ay(t) + \zeta(t), \tag{1.2.1}$$

where $y(t)$ is an $n \times 1$ vector of *random functions* (see Bartlett (1955)) which are observable at integral values of t, $\zeta(t)$ is an $n \times 1$ vector of disturbances which are assumed to have certain stochastic properties, A is an $n \times n$ matrix of parameters and D is an operator premultiplication which is equivalent to some form of *stochastic differentiation* (see Bartlett (1955)). A sequence of observations generated by (1.2.1) satisfies the system

$$y(t) = By(t-1) + \xi(t), \tag{1.2.2}$$

where B is an $n \times n$ matrix of parameters and $\xi(t)$ an $n \times 1$ vector of random disturbances whose properties depend on those of $\zeta(t)$. The argument is, then, that we should specify the model in the form (1.2.2) rather than (1.2.1).

If there were no restrictions on A this argument would be difficult to refute. But the distinguishing feature of econometrics as compared with the application of mathematical statistics in other sciences is the extent to which it makes use of *a priori restrictions* on the parameters of models. Indeed, most of the estimation techniques that have been developed by econometricians can be regarded as methods of using *a priori* information. And there is an obvious reason for this. Whereas the physical scientist is usually able to obtain a sample of whatever size is required in order to give reliable estimates, the econometrician is faced with the task of extracting the maximum amount of information from observations of the economy over a given period. It is very important, therefore, to maximise the number of *degrees of freedom* in the *sample* by making the fullest use of *a priori* information.

The simplest and most common form of *a priori* restriction is that certain variables have no direct causal influence on certain other variables or, more precisely, that certain elements of the matrix A in the system (1.2.1) are zero. But this does not imply that the corresponding elements of B are zero. To assume that they are so would be to make an *error of specification*. Alternatively, to specify the model in the form (1.2.2), but place no restrictions on the elements of B, would involve the neglect of *a priori* information and the estimation of an unnecessarily large number of parameters. Hence the above argument in favour of using systems of difference equations is not a valid one in the case of economic models.

A final argument in favour of formulating models as systems of differential equations is that, even though there are no continuous observations of economic variables, predictions of continuous paths of these variables may be valuable. Suppose, for example, that a firm believes that its sales are closely related to the national income. Then, for the purpose of forecasting sales, it would be useful to have a prediction of a continuous path of the national income, even though the only measurements of this variable are annual ones. A continuous model enables us to extract such a prediction from discrete observations of economic variables over a past period.

In view of the above arguments all of the models to be discussed in this book will be formulated as systems of differential equations. For simplicity we shall omit the disturbances except in the last chapter, where we shall discuss the problem of estimation.

1.3 Economic Theory and Model Construction

The importance of *a priori* information in econometrics has been stressed in the previous section. This information is obtained from various sources including, for example, engineering and physical data, institutional facts and the law. But perhaps the most important source of *a priori* information is the fact that economic behaviour is the result of more or less rational decision-making. The derivation of economic behaviour relations from various axioms of rational economic behaviour is the concern of the more basic branch of *positive* economic theory, *micro-economic* theory. The other branch, *general equilibrium* theory, is concerned with the analysis of the behaviour of the economy that is implied by complete systems of behaviour and technological relations.

The builder of econometric models is concerned with both of these branches of theory. But, unlike the economic theoretician, who usually works with general classes of functions, he must work with particular functional forms (e.g. linear, quadratic, exponential). The functional forms chosen should, in addition to being good approximations to reality, be such that, when the various relations are fitted together, the complete model is amenable to mathematical and statistical analysis.

It might be thought that, if our ultimate concern is with the practical problems of prediction and regulation, there is nothing to be gained from a general analysis of the properties of our models. But such analysis can provide a valuable check on the realism of a model. If, for example, the observations of the variables that are to be explained by it provides evidence of a cycle with a certain period, it will be useful to know whether or not the model is capable of generating such a cycle. Hence much of the book will be devoted to an analysis of the properties of the various models.

CHAPTER 2

MODELS OF A SINGLE SECTOR

THIS chapter has two aims. The first is to construct some simple models that could be used for predicting the behaviour of the main variables (e.g. price, output, profit and capital formation) relating to a single industry, on given assumptions about the behaviour of such variables as the national income and the general price level. The second is to introduce, in a simple setting, certain basic economic concepts and relations which will be used in the subsequent chapters.

2.1 A Simple Model of a Competitive Industry

We shall consider an industry with n firms, each of which produces a single homogeneous product. We assume that the products of the different firms are regarded by consumers as *perfect substitutes*, meaning that no firm can sell any of its product at a price greater than that being charged by another firm in the industry. Under this condition there must be a common selling price applicable to the industry. We assume, moreover, that no firm is sufficiently large in relation to the market to influence the common selling price. Thus each firm must regard the selling price of its product as part of the data affecting its decisions. The other data are the prices payable for *factors of production* (labour, capital and materials) and the technological relations between *inputs* (quantities used) of these factors and the *output* (quantity produced) of the product.

An industry to which the above conditions apply is said to be *perfectly competitive*. In fact, there are very few perfectly competitive industries. In most industries each firm has some control over the price of its product. Nevertheless, there are many industries in which the extent of this control is fairly limited in that each firm's share of the market is very sensitive to small variations in the price of its product relative to the prices of the products of the other firms in the industry. A model incorporating the assumption of perfect competition can be expected to be a useful tool of prediction for such an industry. Moreover, provided that most industries in an economy are fairly competitive, the assumption of perfect competition should provide a useful basis for the construction of a model of the whole economy.

The fundamental economic problem of a firm, in a perfectly competitive industry, is to determine how much of the product to produce and how much of each factor of production to use in order to maximise profit. The models of the firm to be used in this chapter are very simple. They are not intended to be used for the programming of a firm's operations but, rather, for the derivation of certain behaviour relations, expressed in terms of variables relating to an industry or an economy. The predictive power of models incorporating such relations may be high, even though the models of the firm from which they are derived are too simple to be of much use, either for the programming of the operations of an individual firm or the prediction of its behaviour. For example, a model of the firm in which the technological relations between output and inputs are assumed to be continuously differentiable functions may be unrealistic, since it ignores the discontinuities associated with the capacities of various types of equipment. But, if there are many firms in the industry, and the discontinuities relating to different firms become effective at different stages in the expansion or contraction of the industry, the derived model of the industry may, nevertheless, yield good predictions.

In this and the following section we shall assume that the amount of *fixed capital* (buildings, machines and other durable equipment) employed by each firm is constant and that the only variable factors of production are labour and materials. Models involving variations in the amount of fixed capital in the industry will be constructed in sections 2.3 and 2.4.

We assume now that the technological relations applying to the various firms can be approximated, over the relevant ranges of the variables, by the equations

$$M_i = m_i Q_i \qquad (i = 1, \ldots, n), \tag{2.1.1}$$

$$L_i = a_i + b_i Q_i + c_i Q_i^2 \qquad (i = 1, \ldots, n), \tag{2.1.2}$$

where Q_i = output (per unit of time) by firm i,

L_i = amount of labour employed by firm i,

M_i = quantity of material used (per unit of time) by firm i,

m_i, a_i, b_i, c_i = positive constants.

Equation (2.1.2) implies the L_i/Q_i is a decreasing function of Q_i for $Q_i < \sqrt{a_i/c_i}$ and an increasing function of Q_i for $Q_i > \sqrt{a_i/c_i}$. It follows that output per unit of labour is assumed to be an increasing or decreasing function of the amount of labour employed according as this amount is less or greater than $2a_i + b_i\sqrt{a_i/c_i}$. There are good reasons for expecting this type of relation. As the amount of labour employed increases, output per man hour can be expected to increase, up to a certain point, because of the increasing *division of labour*. But there is, normally, a maximum amount that can be produced with the given capital equipment, and there are various reasons why output per man hour might decrease as this maximum is approached. Perhaps the most important is that, whenever a firm has several different machines that can be used for performing a given operation, the least efficient of these will be used only when production is at peak levels.

We assume next that each firm adjusts its output in response to variations in the price of the product, the wage rate and the price of material in such a way as to maximise profit as defined by

(2.1.3) $$P_i = pQ_i - wL_i - p_m M_i \qquad (i = 1, \ldots, n),$$

where P_i = profit of firm i,
p = price of product,
w = wage rate,
p_m = price of material.

We shall confine our attention to the range of prices within which every firm can make a profit.

From (2.1.1), (2.1.2) and (2.1.3) we obtain

(2.1.4) $$P_i = (p - m_i p_m - b_i w)Q_i - c_i w Q_i^2 - a_i w.$$

And from (2.1.4) and the assumption of profit maximisation we obtain:

(2.1.5) $$\frac{dP_i}{dQ_i} = p - m_i p_m - b_i w - 2c_i w Q_i = 0,$$

and hence

(2.1.6) $$Q_i = \frac{p - m_i p_m}{2c_i w} - \frac{b_i}{2c_i} \qquad (i = 1, \ldots, n).$$

Finally we obtain

(2.1.7) $$Q = \frac{fp - gp_m}{w} - h,$$

where $$Q = \sum_{i=1}^{n} Q_i = \text{industry output}$$

$$f = \sum_{i=1}^{n}\left(\frac{1}{2c_i}\right)$$

$$g = \sum_{i=1}^{n}\left(\frac{m_i}{2c_i}\right)$$

$$h = \sum_{i=1}^{n}\left(\frac{b_i}{2c_i}\right).$$

The last equation expresses the industry output as a function of the product price, the wage rate, the price of material and the technological parameters. This function will be referred to as the *supply function*. We note that it has the following properties:

(i) it is homogeneous of degree zero in p, p_m and w;

(ii) $\frac{\partial Q}{\partial p} > 0$, (iii) $\frac{\partial Q}{\partial p_m} < 0$, (iv) $\frac{\partial Q}{\partial w} < 0$ if $fp > gp_m$ (which is necessary for $Q > 0$)

We turn now to the demand side of the model. We could proceed with a formal derivation of a *demand function* similar to that given for the supply function. Each consumer would be assumed to allocate his expenditure between different goods in such a way as to maximise his satisfaction or *utility* which we would assume to be a certain function of the quantities of the various goods consumed by him. We could then derive the demand for each good, by any consumer, as function of his income and the prices of the various goods (see Hicks (1946) and Samuelson (1948)). The market demand for the good could then be expressed as a function of the prices of the various goods and the incomes of the various consumers. But, even if the consumers in the market can be divided into a small number of homogeneous groups, the estimation of the parameters of such a function is normally impracticable unless we are constructing a multi-sector model.

The impracticability arises from the fact that, unless we use data relating to the sales of all of the goods in the market, and estimate the parameters of the complete system of demand equations simultaneously, there will normally be insufficient degrees of freedom in a sample to yield reliable estimates. Further discussion of this type of analysis will be postponed, therefore, until Chapter 8. In each of the models to be discussed in this chapter we shall assume that the demand for the product of the industry under discussion is a function of three variables: the price of this product, the total income of consumers in the market and an arbitrary index of the prices of all other consumers' goods in the market. Empirical studies indicate that a high proportion of the variance of demand for a consumers' good can usually be explained by a simple function involving these variables and, perhaps, the prices of one or two closely related goods (see Wold (1952) and Stone (1954a)). The function is usually assumed to be homogeneous of the degree zero, this property being implied by the theory of utility maximisation.

It will be convenient, in the model under discussion, to assume that the demand function is also linear in income and in the price of the product. We assume, therefore, that

$$(2.1.8) \qquad X = \frac{kY - lp}{p_0} + m,$$

where $X = \sum_{i=1}^{n} X_i,$

$X_i =$ sales of product of firm i,

$Y =$ income,

$p_0 =$ index of prices of all other consumers' goods.

$k, l, m =$ positive constants

This equation implies that $\frac{\partial X}{\partial Y} > 0$ and $\frac{\partial X}{\partial p} < 0$. Although these properties are not necessary implications of the theory of utility maximisation, empirical evidence indicates that they are satisfied for most consumers' goods.

We assume that the product of the industry can be stored, so that $Q_i - X_i$ is the rate of increase in the stock of the product of firm i. An explanation of the behaviour of the individual X_i's will not be given by the formal model. Although we have formally assumed that there is a common selling price, p for the products of the firms in the industry, there will, in most industries, be small variations in the relative prices of the products of different firms, and these could ensure that the X_i's are always approximately proportional to the Q_i's, so that the stocks held by different firms tend to increase or decrease together.

In order to complete the formal model we require a price adjustment equation which shows how p varies in response to changes in the other variables. A simple and widely used assumption is that the rate of increase in the price is proportional to the excess of sales over production (see, for example, Samuelson (1941)). This is represented by the equation

$$Dp = \gamma(X - Q), \tag{2.1.9}$$

where D denotes the differential operator, d/dt.

Equation (2.1.9) can be regarded as reflecting the independent pricing decisions of the firms in response to the excess demands for their respective products. This interpretation is realistic only if small variations in the relative prices of the products of different firms are, in fact, possible as envisaged in the preceding paragraph. For no firm can be sure that, if it raises the price of its product, its competitors will do likewise. An alternative interpretation is that there is a trader or small group of traders who play the role of a middleman, buying the total output of producers at a uniform price and selling whatever quantity is demanded by consumers at this price plus a certain margin. The equation then represents the continuous adjustment of the price by the middleman in response to variations in his stocks. The latter interpretation is, perhaps, most relevant to farming and other primary product industries.

Equations (2.1.7), (2.1.8) and (2.1.9) provide a simple model of a competitive industry. Together they determine the dynamic behaviour of Q, X and p in response to any assumed behaviour of w, p_m, p_0 and Y. The last four variables are assumed to be *exogenous* in the sense that they are determined by relations outside the model. The variables Q, X and p, whose paths are determined by the model, are called *endogenous* variables.

We shall examine the behaviour of the endogenous variables, first for the case in which the exogenous variables are constant. Solving (2.1.7),

(2.1.8) and (2.1.9), together with $Dp = 0$ we obtain the particular solution, p^*, X^*, Q^*, where

$$(2.1.10) \qquad p^* = \frac{kwY + gp_m p_0 + (m+h)p_0 w}{lw + fp_0},$$

$$(2.1.11) \qquad Q^* = X^* = \frac{f\{kY + (h+m)p_0\} - glp_m}{lw + fp_0} - h.$$

We shall call p^*, Q^* and X^* the *equilibrium* price, output and sales respectively. It is clear from (2.1.11) that, if $f\{kY + (h+m)p_0\} > glp_m$ (which is necessary for $Q^* > 0$), then $\frac{\partial Q^*}{\partial w} = \frac{\partial X^*}{\partial w} < 0$. It then follows, with the help of (2.1.8), that $\frac{\partial p^*}{\partial w} > 0$. And it is clear from (2.1.10) and (2.1.11) that $\frac{\partial p^*}{\partial Y} > 0$, $\frac{\partial p^*}{\partial p_m} > 0$, $\frac{\partial Q^*}{\partial Y} > 0$ and $\frac{\partial Q^*}{\partial p_m} < 0$.

We turn now to the general solution assuming, still, that the exogenous variables are constant. From equations (2.1.7) to (2.1.9) we obtain

$$(2.1.12) \qquad \left\{D + \gamma\left(\frac{l}{p_0} + \frac{f}{w}\right)\right\}p = \gamma\left(\frac{kY}{p_0} + \frac{gp_m}{w} + h + m\right),$$

whose solution is

$$(2.1.13) \qquad p = p^* + \{p(0) - p^*\}e^{-\gamma(l/p_0 + f/w)t},$$

where $p(0)$ is the initial value of p. And from (2.1.7), (2.1.8) and (2.1.13) we obtain

$$(2.1.14) \qquad Q = Q^* + \{Q(0) - Q^*\}e^{-\gamma(l/p_0 + f/w)t},$$

$$(2.1.15) \qquad X = X^* + \{X(0) - X^*\}e^{-\gamma(l/p_0 + f/w)t}.$$

The initial output, sales and price must, of course, satisfy (2.1.7) and (2.1.8).

The above solution implies that, if the exogenous variables are constant, the output, sales and price converge steadily to their equilibrium levels. In fact the exogenous variables will seldom be constant, and one of the main practical applications of the type of model under discussion will be the prediction of the behaviour of Q, X and p under certain assumptions about the behaviour of Y, p_0, w and p_m. The assumptions about the behaviour of the exogenous variables may, themselves, be predictions that have been obtained from models of the types discussed in later chapters.

Suppose, for example, that, over the time interval $(0, T)$, Y is expected to grow at the proportional rate ρ, while p_0, p_m and w are expected to remain constant. The predicted path of p over the interval $(0, T)$ then satisfies

$$(2.1.16) \quad \left\{D + \gamma\left(\frac{l}{p_0} + \frac{f}{w}\right)\right\}p = \gamma\left(\frac{kY(0)e^{\rho t}}{p_0} + \frac{gp_m}{w} + h + m\right),$$

whose solution is

$$(2.1.17) \quad p = p^{**} + \{p(0) - p^{**}(0)\}e^{-\gamma(l/p_0 + f/w)t},$$

where

$$(2.1.18) \quad p^{**} = \frac{\gamma kwY(0)e^{\rho t}}{\rho p_0 w + \gamma(lw + fp_0)} + \frac{gp_m p_0 + (m + h)p_0 w}{lw + fp_0}.$$

2.2 The Influence of Stocks

It was assumed, in equation (2.1.9), that the rate of increase in price is proportional to the excess of sales over production. But, in fact, the price may change, even when sales and production are equal, if the stock level is considered to be too high or too low. A more general form of price adjustment equation (cf. Samuelson (1941)) which takes account of the influence of stocks is

$$(2.2.1) \quad Dp = \gamma(X - Q) + \lambda(S^0 - S),$$

where S denotes the actual stock level and S^0 the desired or optimum level. The latter will usually depend on sales and also on the cost of holding stock, the degree of uncertainty about the future and various other factors which we assume to be constant. We assume that the relation between S^0 and X can be adequately represented by the equation

$$(2.2.2) \quad S^0 = uX + v,$$

where u and v are positive constants. The revised model is completed by the equation

$$(2.2.3) \quad DS = Q - X.$$

The complete model now comprises equations (2.1.7), (2.1.8), (2.2.1), (2.2.2) and (2.2.3) which determine the paths of Q, X, p, S and S^0 for any assumed behaviour of the exogenous variables. By eliminating Q, X and S^0 we obtain the system

$$(2.2.4) \quad \left[D + \left\{\frac{l(\gamma + \lambda u)}{p_0} + \frac{\gamma f}{w}\right\}\right]p + \lambda S = (\gamma + \lambda u)\left(\frac{kY}{p_0} + m\right) + \gamma\left(\frac{gp_m}{w} + h\right) + \lambda v,$$

$$2.2.5) \quad DS - \left(\frac{f}{w} + \frac{l}{p_0}\right)p = -\frac{gp_m}{w} - \frac{kY}{p_0} - h - m,$$

which determines the paths of S and p.

Consider now the case in which the exogenous variables are constant. Putting $Dp = DS = 0$ in (2.2.4) and (2.2.5), and solving for p and S we obtain the particular solution (p^*, S^*), where p^* is given by (2.1.10) and S^* by

$$S^* = \frac{u}{fp_0 + lw}[f\{kY + (h + m)p_0\} - glp_m] - uh + v. \tag{2.2.6}$$

Then, from (2.2.4), (2.2.5), (2.1.10) and (2.2.6) we obtain

$$\left[D + \left\{\frac{l(\gamma + \lambda u)}{p_0} + \frac{\gamma f}{w}\right\}\right](p - p^*) + \lambda(S - S^*) = 0, \tag{2.2.7}$$

$$D(S - S^*) - \left(\frac{f}{w} + \frac{l}{p_0}\right)(p - p^*) = 0. \tag{2.2.8}$$

Differentiating (2.2.7) and combining with (2.2.8) we obtain

$$\left[D^2 + \left\{\frac{l(\gamma + \lambda u)}{p_0} + \frac{\gamma f}{w}\right\}D + \lambda\left(\frac{f}{w} + \frac{l}{p_0}\right)\right](p - p^*) = 0, \tag{2.2.9}$$

whose solution is

$$p = p^* + A_1 e^{x_1 t} + A_2 e^{x_2 t}, \tag{2.2.10}$$

where

$$A_1 = \frac{x_2\{p(0) - p^*\} - p'(0)}{x_2 - x_1}$$

$$= \frac{1}{x_2 - x_1}\left[\left\{x_2 + \frac{l(\gamma + \lambda u)}{p_0} + \frac{\gamma f}{w}\right\}\{p(0) - p^*\} + \lambda\{S(0) - S^*\}\right],$$

$$A_2 = \frac{1}{x_1 - x_2}\left[\left\{x_1 + \frac{l(\gamma + \lambda u)}{p_0} + \frac{\gamma f}{w}\right\}\{p(0) - p^*\} + \lambda\{S(0) - S^*\}\right],$$

and x_1 and x_2 are the roots of

$$x^2 + \left\{\frac{l(\gamma + \lambda u)}{p_0} + \frac{\gamma f}{w}\right\}x + \lambda\left(\frac{f}{w} + \frac{l}{p_0}\right) = 0. \tag{2.2.11}$$

Equation (2.2.10) expresses p as a function of t and the initial values, $p(0)$ and $S(0)$ or, using (2.1.7) and (2.1.8), as a function of t, $S(0)$ and any one of $p(0)$, $Q(0)$ and $X(0)$. By substituting from (2.2.10) into (2.1.7) and (2.1.8) we obtain $Q(t)$ and $X(t)$. Since all the coefficients of (2.2.11) are positive, the roots, x_1 and x_2 have negative real parts. It follows that the system is *stable* in the sense that the variables tend to their equilibrium values as $t \longrightarrow \infty$. But x_1 and x_2 can be either real or complex, depending on the values of the parameters. Hence the paths of the variables can be oscillatory. It is clear, however, that oscillations will not occur if λ, which measures the influence of stocks on the rate of price adjustment, is sufficiently small.

As an example of the application of the model to a situation in which the exogenous variables are not all constant, we consider again the problem of predicting the behaviour of p, X and Q when Y is expected to increase at the constant proportional rate ρ, and p_0, p_m and w to remain constant. The predicted paths of p and S are given by the solution of the system

$$(2.2.12)\quad \left[D+\left\{\frac{l(\gamma+\lambda u)}{p_0}+\frac{\gamma f}{w}\right\}\right]p+\lambda S = (\gamma+\lambda u)\left\{\frac{kY(0)e^{\rho t}}{p_0}+m\right\}+\gamma\left\{\frac{gp_m}{w}+h\right\}+\lambda v,$$

$$(2.2.13)\quad DS-\left(\frac{f}{w}+\frac{l}{p_0}\right)p=-\frac{kY(0)e^{\rho t}}{p_0}-\frac{gp_m}{w}-h-m,$$

which is obtained from (2.2.4) and (2.2.5) by substituting $Y = Y(0)e^{\rho t}$. This system, evidently, has a particular solution (p^{**}, S^{**}) where p^{**} and S^{**} are linear functions of $e^{\rho t}$ with constant coefficients. By substituting these functions into (2.2.12) and (2.2.13) and solving for the unknown coefficients we obtain

$$(2.2.14)\quad p^{**}=\frac{\{\rho(\gamma+\lambda u)+\lambda\}kwY(0)e^{\rho t}}{\{\rho(\gamma+\lambda u)+\lambda\}(fp_0+lw)+\rho^2p_0w-\rho\lambda ufp_0}+\frac{gp_0p_m+p_0w(h+m)}{fp_0+lw},$$

$$(2.2.15)\quad S^{**}=\frac{(\lambda uf-\rho w)kY(0)e^{\rho t}}{\{\rho(\gamma+\lambda u)+\lambda\}(fp_0+lw)+\rho^2p_0w-\rho\lambda ufp_0}+\frac{u(fmp_0-glp_m-hlw)}{fp_0+lw}+v.$$

From equations (2.2.12) to (2.2.15) we obtain the system

$$(2.2.16)\quad \left[D+\left\{\frac{l(\gamma+\lambda u)}{p_0}+\frac{\gamma f}{w}\right\}\right](p-p^{**})+\lambda(S-S^{**})=0,$$

$$(2.2.17)\quad D(S-S^{**})-\left(\frac{f}{w}+\frac{l}{p_0}\right)(p-p^{**})=0,$$

whose solution, for p, is

$$(2.2.18)\quad p=p^{**}+B_1e^{x_1t}+B_2e^{x_2t},$$

where

$$B_1=\frac{1}{x_2-x_1}\left[\left\{x_2+\frac{l(\gamma+\lambda u)}{p_0}+\frac{\gamma f}{w}\right\}\{p(0)-p^{**}(0)\}+\lambda\{S(0)-S^{**}(0)\}\right],$$

$$B_2=\frac{1}{x_1-x_2}\left[\left\{x_1+\frac{l(\gamma+\lambda u)}{p_0}+\frac{\gamma f}{w}\right\}\{p(0)-p^{**}(0)\}+\lambda\{S(0)-S^{**}(0)\}\right],$$

and x_1 and x_2 are the roots of (2.2.11). The predicted paths of Q and X are obtained by substituting from (2.2.18) into (2.1.7) and (2.1.8) and putting $Y = Y(0)e^{\rho t}$ in (2.1.8).

2.3 Variations in the Amount of Fixed Capital

It has been assumed, so far, that each firm in the industry has a given amount of fixed capital and that all variations in output are obtained by varying the inputs of labour and materials. In the model to be constructed in this section we shall make the more realistic assumption that the amount of fixed capital varies continuously and is determined, together with the other endogenous variables, by the model.

It will be convenient, at this stage, to introduce the concept of a production function. Two alternative ways of treating the technical relations between inputs and outputs are commonly employed in economic models. The first is to assume equations of the form

$$(2.3.1) \qquad L_{ij} = f_{ij}(Q_i) \qquad (i = 1, \ldots, n), \quad (j = 1, \ldots, m),$$

where L_{ij} = input of factor j by firm i,

Q_i = output by firm i.

This is the method employed in the models constructed in sections 2.1 and 2.2. It has the advantage of simplicity, but is unrealistic in that it does not allow for the possibility of substitution between factors of production. In fact, most factors of production can, to some extent, be replaced by other factors. It is possible, for example, by employing more capital and using more mechanised techniques of production, to produce the same output with less labour or, by using more labour to produce the same output with less materials, by reducing waste. The second method allows for such substitution between factors by assuming equations of the form

$$(2.3.2) \qquad Q_i = f_i(L_{i1}, L_{i2}, \ldots, L_{im}) \qquad (i = 1, \ldots, n).$$

The function f_i in (2.3.2) is known as a *production function* and its partial derivative $\frac{\partial Q_i}{\partial L_{ij}}$ as the *marginal product* of factor j. The ratio $\frac{\partial Q_i}{\partial L_{ih}} \Big/ \frac{\partial Q_i}{\partial L_{ij}}$ is known as the *marginal rate of substitution of factor h for factor j*. It is approximately equal to the decrease in the input of factor j made possible by a small unit increase in the input of factor h, if output is to be unchanged. Empirical evidence suggests that most production functions have the property that, when the input of factor h is increased and the input of factor j decreased, in such a way as to leave both the inputs of other factors and the output unchanged, then the marginal rate of substitution of factor h for factor j diminishes. This is known as *the law of diminishing marginal rate of substitution.* It is expressed more precisely by

(2.3.3) $$\frac{d\left\{\frac{\partial Q_i}{\partial L_{ih}}\bigg/\frac{\partial Q_i}{\partial L_{ij}}\right\}}{d\left\{\frac{L_{ih}}{L_{ij}}\right\}} < 0,$$

where, for the purpose of defining the simple derivative, Q_i and the L_{ik}'s $(k \neq h, j)$ are held constant. A measure of the degree of substitutability between factors h and j is given by the *elasticity of substitution*, ε_{ihj}, which is defined by

(2.3.4) $$\varepsilon_{ihj} = \frac{d\left\{\frac{L_{ih}}{L_{ij}}\right\}}{d\left\{\frac{\partial Q_i}{\partial L_{ih}}\bigg/\frac{\partial Q_i}{\partial L_{ij}}\right\}} \times \frac{\frac{\partial Q_i}{\partial L_{ih}}\bigg/\frac{\partial Q_i}{\partial L_{ij}}}{\frac{L_{ih}}{L_{ij}}}.$$

In the limiting case in which the marginal rate of substitution is independent of the quantities of the factors used, so that the elasticity of substitution is infinite, the factors are said to be *perfect substitutes.*

Production functions are often assumed to be homogeneous of the first degree, and, in this case, are said to show *constant returns to scale.* As an example of a production function that shows constant returns to scale and obeys the law of diminishing marginal rate of substitution we have

(2.3.5) $$Q_i = A \prod_{j=i}^{m} L_{ij}^{\alpha_j} \qquad 0 < \alpha_j < 1 \text{ for } j = 1, \ldots, m,$$
$$\sum_{j=1}^{m} \alpha_j = 1.$$

This is known as a Cobb–Douglas production function. Because of its convenient mathematical properties it is widely used. But it is rather restrictive since it implies that the elasticity of substitution is equal to unity. A more general form of production function in which the elasticity of substitution is constant, but not necessarily equal to unity, was proposed by Arrow, Chenery, Minhas and Solow (1961).

In the following model we shall assume that the output of each firm in the industry is related to the amounts of labour and fixed capital by a Cobb–Douglas production function, and, for simplicity, that the industry uses no other factors of production. In order to keep the model as simple as possible while retaining its essential features we shall assume, also, that the technical and behaviour relations applying to different firms in the industry are identical. The model can then be formulated directly in terms of the aggregate inputs and output of the industry.

The production relation is

(2.3.6) $$Q = AL^a K^{(1-a)},$$

where Q = industry output,

L = amount of labour employed by industry,

K = amount of fixed capital employed by industry,

A, a = positive constants ($a < 1$).

Assuming now that, at every point of time, each firm produces at a rate that maximises its profit, taking the product price, the wage rate and its stock of capital as given, we have

(2.3.7) $$\frac{dP}{dQ} = 0,$$

where

(2.3.8) $$P = pQ - wL$$
$$= pQ - w\left\{\frac{Q}{A}\right\}^{1/a} K^{(a-1)/a},$$

and p and w are the price and wage rate respectively. We assume that, although each firm can vary the amount of its fixed capital, only the rate of change of this variable can be varied instantaneously. At any point of time, therefore, the firm must regard the amount of fixed capital as part of the data affecting its decisions. From (2.3.7) and (2.3.8) we obtain the supply equation,

(2.3.9) $$Q = A^{1/(1-a)} K\left\{\frac{ap}{w}\right\}^{a/(1-a)}.$$

As in the case of (2.1.7) we have $\frac{\partial Q}{\partial p} > 0$, $\frac{\partial Q}{\partial w} < 0$ and homogeneity of degree zero in the prices. But now the supply function involves the variable K, and we have $\frac{\partial Q}{\partial K} > 0$.

We require, next, an equation reflecting the firms' decisions with respect to investment in fixed capital. We assume that

(2.3.10) $$\frac{DK}{K} = b \log\left\{\frac{P}{(1+c)rp_k K}\right\},$$

where r = rate of interest,

p_k = price of capital goods,

b, c = positive constants.

This equation implies that the proportional rate of increase in the amount of fixed capital in the industry is greater, the greater is $\frac{P}{p_k K}$, the rate of profit on the existing capital and the lower is r, the rate of interest at which firms can borrow. The term $(1 + c)r$ is the rate of profit required by firms to induce them to maintain the existing amount of fixed capital. If the rate of profit falls below $(1 + c)r$, some capital goods will not be replaced as they wear out, and DK will be negative, while, if the rate of profit exceeds $(1 + c)r$, purchases of new capital goods will exceed replacement requirements, and DK will be positive. The constant c can be interpreted as a risk premium. The variables r and p_k will be treated as exogenous.

We shall refer to the function on the right-hand side of (2.3.10) as the *investment function*. A logarithmic investment function, in addition to being mathematically convenient, in the model under discussion, is, perhaps, more realistic than a linear function. For there are various reasons (such as the risk associated with a high proportional rate of increase in K) for expecting the second derivative of the function with respect to the rate of profit to be negative.

We assume, as in the previous models, that the sales of the industry is a function of income, the price of the product of the industry and an index of the prices of all other consumers' goods, and, in particular, that

$$X = BY^f p^{-g} p_0^{g-f}, \tag{2.3.11}$$

where B, f and g are positive constants. Thus the demand function is assumed, as in (2.1.8), to be homogeneous of the degree zero in Y, p and p_0. It also has the property that the *income elasticity of demand*, $\left\{\frac{\partial X}{\partial Y}\right\} \Big/ \left\{\frac{X}{Y}\right\}$, and *price elasticity of demand*, $\left\{\frac{\partial X}{\partial p}\right\} \Big/ \left\{\frac{X}{p}\right\}$, are constants. This type of demand function has been extensively used in empirical demand studies (see, for example, Wold (1952) and Stone (1954a)).

We complete the model by assuming the price adjustment equation

$$\begin{aligned} \frac{Dp}{p} &= \gamma \log\left(1 + \frac{X - Q}{Q}\right) \\ &= \gamma \log\left(\frac{X}{Q}\right) \end{aligned} \tag{2.3.12}$$

where γ is a positive constant. This equation, like (2.1.9), implies that the price will be constant when sales and production are equal. But, instead of assuming that the rate of increase in price is a function of the excess of sales over production, we assume, in (2.3.12), that the proportional rate of increase in price is a function of the proportional excess of sales over production. The complete model comprises equations (2.3.6) and (2.3.8) to (2.3.12) and determines the behaviour of Q, X, L, K, p and P for any assumed behaviour of the exogenous variables.

Eliminating w from (2.3.8) and (2.3.9) we obtain

$$P = (1 - a)pQ, \tag{2.3.13}$$

which means that profit is a constant proportion of the total value of output. This is a well-known implication of the assumptions of perfect competition and a Cobb–Douglas production function.

From (2.3.10) and (2.3.13) we obtain

$$\frac{DK}{K} = b \log \left\{ \frac{(1 - a)pQ}{(1 + c)rp_k K} \right\}. \tag{2.3.14}$$

Then, from (2.3.6), (2.3.9), (2.3.11), (2.3.12) and (2.3.14), we obtain the system

$$\log Q - a \log L - (1 - a) \log K = \log A, \tag{2.3.15}$$

$$\log Q - \log K - \frac{a}{1 - a} \log p = - \frac{a}{1 - a} \log w + \frac{1}{1 - a} (\log A + a \log a), \tag{2.3.16}$$

$$\log X + g \log p = f \log Y + (g - f) \log p_0 + \log B, \tag{2.3.17}$$

$$D \log p + \gamma (\log Q - \log X) = 0, \tag{2.3.18}$$

$$(D + b) \log K - b (\log Q + \log p) = -b \log \{(1 + c)rp_k\} + b \log (1 - a), \tag{2.3.19}$$

which is linear in the logarithms of the variables. Eliminating Q and X from equations (2.3.16) to (2.3.19) we obtain the system

$$\left[D + \gamma \left\{ \frac{a}{1 - a} + g \right\} \right] \log p + \gamma \log K = \frac{\gamma a}{1 - a} \log w + \gamma f \log Y + \gamma (g - f) \log p_0 - \frac{\gamma}{1 - a} (\log A + a \log a) + \gamma \log B, \tag{2.3.20}$$

$$D \log K - \frac{b}{1 - a} \log p = - \frac{ab}{1 - a} \log w - b \log \{(1 + c)rp_k\} + \frac{b}{1 - a} (\log A + a \log a) + b \log (1 - a), \tag{2.3.21}$$

which determines the paths of p and K.

Assuming the exogenous variables to be constant, putting $D \log p = D \log K = 0$ and solving for $\log p$ and $\log K$ we obtain

$$\log p^* = a \log w + (1 - a) \log \{(1 + c)rp_k\} - \log A - a \log a - (1 - a) \log (1 - a), \tag{2.3.22}$$

$$\text{(2.3.23)}\quad \log K^* = a(1-g)\log w - \{a+g(1-a)\}\log\{(1+c)rp_k\} + f\log Y + (g-f)\log p_0 + (g-1)\{\log A + a\log a\} + \{a+g(1-a)\}\log(1-a) + \log B.$$

Then, from (2.3.15), (2.3.16), (2.3.22) and (2.3.23) we obtain

$$\text{(2.3.24)}\quad \log L^* = -(1-a+ag)\log w + (1-a)(1-g)\log\{(1+c)rp_k\} + f\log Y + (g-f)\log p_0 + (g-1)\{\log A + (1-a)\log(1-a)\} + (1-a+ag)\log a + \log B,$$

$$\text{(2.3.25)}\quad \log Q^* = -ag\log w - g(1-a)\log\{(1+c)rp_k\} + f\log Y + (g-f)\log p_0 + \log B + g\{\log A + a\log a + (1-a)\log(1-a)\}.$$

Equation (2.3.22) implies that p^* is proportional to a weighted geometric mean of w and $(1+c)rp_k$, and is independent of Y and p_0. The term $(1+c)rp_k$ can be interpreted as the cost (including a risk premium) of employing a unit of fixed capital. As might be expected, we have $\frac{\partial Q^*}{\partial w} < 0$, $\frac{\partial Q^*}{\partial(rp_k)} < 0$, $\frac{\partial Q^*}{\partial Y} > 0$, $\frac{\partial K^*}{\partial(rp_k)} < 0$, $\frac{\partial K^*}{\partial Y} > 0$, $\frac{\partial L^*}{\partial w} < 0$, $\frac{\partial L^*}{\partial Y} > 0$, and $\frac{\partial Q^*}{\partial p_0}$, $\frac{\partial K^*}{\partial p_0}$ and $\frac{\partial L^*}{\partial p_0}$ of indeterminate sign. The signs of $\frac{\partial K^*}{\partial w}$ and $\frac{\partial L^*}{\partial(rp_k)}$ are also indeterminate. The reason why the sign of $\frac{\partial K^*}{\partial w}$ $\left(\text{and, by a symmetrical argument, the sign of } \frac{\partial L^*}{\partial(rp_k)}\right)$ is indeterminate is that an increase in w, when all other exogenous variables are held constant, will affect K^* in two different ways. First, it will cause a decrease in Q^*, and, if $\frac{K^*}{L^*}$ were constant, this would cause a decrease in K^*. Secondly, it will cause an increase in $\frac{K^*}{L^*}$. These two effects are known as the *scale* and *substitution* effects respectively. The substitution effect is implicit in the equation

$$\text{(2.3.26)}\quad \frac{K^*}{L^*} = \frac{(1-a)w}{a(1+c)rp_k},$$

which follows from (2.3.23) and (2.3.24).

Equation (2.3.26) shows that the equilibrium ratio of capital to labour is an increasing function of the ratio of the wage rate to the cost of employing a unit of capital. It can be written in the alternative form

$$\text{(2.3.27)}\quad \frac{aK^*}{(1-a)L^*} = \frac{w}{(1+c)rp_k},$$

which means that, when the system is in equilibrium, the marginal rate of substitution of labour for capital equals the ratio of their unit costs.

The last condition implies that, when the system is in equilibrium, the *unit cost of production*, C, defined by

$$C = \frac{wL + (1+c)rp_k K}{Q} = \frac{w + (1+c)rp_k\left\{\frac{K}{L}\right\}}{A\left\{\frac{K}{L}\right\}^{1-a}}, \tag{2.3.28}$$

is at a minimum with respect to $\frac{K}{L}$. From (2.3.26) and (2.3.28) we obtain

$$C^* = \frac{w^a\{(1+c)rp_k\}^{1-a}}{Aa^a(1-a)^{1-a}} = \underset{K/L}{\text{Min}}\ C. \tag{2.3.29}$$

Moreover, from (2.3.22) and (2.3.29) we have

$$p^* = C^* = \underset{K/L}{\text{Min}}\ C. \tag{2.3.30}$$

The last result explains why p^* is independent of Y and p_0. The equilibrium price equals the minimum unit cost of production which, because of constant returns to scale, is independent of output.

From equations (2.3.20) to (2.3.23) we obtain

$$\left[D + \gamma\left\{\frac{a}{1-a} + g\right\}\right] \log\left\{\frac{p}{p^*}\right\} + \gamma \log\left\{\frac{K}{K^*}\right\} = 0, \tag{2.3.31}$$

$$D \log\left\{\frac{K}{K^*}\right\} - \frac{b}{1-a} \log\left\{\frac{p}{p^*}\right\} = 0, \tag{2.3.32}$$

Hence we obtain

$$\left[D^2 + \gamma\left\{\frac{a}{1-a} + g\right\}D + \frac{\gamma b}{1-a}\right] \log\left\{\frac{p}{p^*}\right\} = 0, \tag{2.3.33}$$

whose solution is

$$\log p = \log p^* + A_1 e^{x_1 t} + A_2 e^{x_2 t}, \tag{2.3.34}$$

where

$$A_1 = \frac{1}{x_2 - x_1}\left[\left\{x_2 + \frac{\gamma a}{1-a} + \gamma g\right\} \log\left\{\frac{p(0)}{p^*}\right\} + \gamma \log\left\{\frac{K(0)}{K^*}\right\}\right],$$

$$A_2 = \frac{1}{x_1 - x_2}\left[\left\{x_1 + \frac{\gamma a}{1-a} + \gamma g\right\} \log\left\{\frac{p(0)}{p^*}\right\} + \gamma \log\left\{\frac{K(0)}{K^*}\right\}\right],$$

and x_1 and x_2 are the roots of

$$x^2 + \gamma\left\{\frac{a}{1-a} + g\right\}x + \frac{\gamma b}{1-a} = 0. \tag{2.3.35}$$

Equation (2.3.34) expresses p as a function of t, $K(0)$ and $p(0)$, or, by using (2.3.15) to (2.3.17), as a function of t, $K(0)$ and any one of $X(0)$, $Q(0)$, $L(0)$ and $p(0)$. By using (2.3.32), (2.3.34) and (2.3.15) to (2.3.17) we can obtain $K(t)$, $X(t)$, $Q(t)$ and $L(t)$. We note that the proportional deviation of each endogenous variable from its equilibrium value is a function of the proportional deviations of the initial values of these variables from their equilibrium values. Moreover, since the coefficients of (2.3.35) are positive, the system is stable. The roots of (2.3.35) may be complex so that, as in the previous model, the paths of the variables may be oscillatory. It can be seen that, for given values of a and g, the possibility of complex roots depends on the magnitude of $\frac{b}{\gamma}$. Hence oscillations will occur if the speed of adjustment of the amount of fixed capital, in response to the rate of profit, is sufficiently great relative to the speed of adjustment of the price in response to excess demand.

As an example of the application of the model to a situation in which the exogenous variables are not all constant, we shall consider the problem of predicting the behaviour of p, K, X, Q and L when Y and w are expected to increase at the constant proportional rates ρ_1 and ρ_2 respectively, and p_0, p_k and r to remain constant. The predicted paths of p and K are given by the solution of the system

$$(2.3.36)\quad \left[D + \gamma\left\{\frac{a}{1-a} + g\right\}\right] \log p + \gamma \log K$$
$$= \frac{\gamma a}{1-a}\{\log w(0) + \rho_2 t\} + \gamma f\{\log Y(0) + \rho_1 t\}$$
$$+ \gamma(g-f)\log p_0 - \frac{\gamma}{1-a}(\log A + a \log a) + \gamma \log B,$$

$$(2.3.37)\quad D \log K - \frac{b}{1-a}\log p = -\frac{ab}{1-a}\{\log w(0) + \rho_2 t\}$$
$$-b \log\{(1+c)rp_k\} + \frac{b}{1-a}(\log A + a \log a) + b \log(1-a),$$

which is obtained from (2.3.20) and (2.3.21) by substituting $Y = Y(0)e^{\rho_1 t}$ and $w = w(0)e^{\rho_2 t}$. This system has a particular solution, (p^{**}, K^{**}), where $\log p^{**}$ and $\log K^{**}$ are linear functions of t with constant coefficients. By substituting these functions into (2.3.36) and (2.3.37) and solving for the unknown coefficients we obtain

$$(2.3.38)\quad \log p^{**} = a\rho_2 t + a \log w(0) + (1-a)\log\{(1+c)rp_k\}$$
$$- \log A - a \log a - (1-a)\log(1-a)$$
$$+ \frac{1-a}{b}\{f\rho_1 + a(1-g)\rho_2\},$$

$$(2.3.39)\quad \log K^{**} = \{f\rho_1 + a(1-g)\rho_2\}t + a(1-g)\log w(0) - \{a+g(1-a)\}\log\{(1+c)r p_k\} + f\log Y(0) + (g-f)\log p_0 + (g-1)(\log A + a\log a) + \{a+g(1-a)\}\log(1-a) + \log B - \frac{f}{b}\{a+g(1-a)\}\rho_1 - \left[\frac{a(1-g)}{b}\{a+g(1-a)\} + \frac{a}{\gamma}\right]\rho_2.$$

From equations (2.3.36) to (2.3.39) we obtain

$$(2.3.40)\quad \left[D + \gamma\left\{\frac{a}{1-a} + g\right\}\right]\log\left\{\frac{p}{p^{**}}\right\} + \gamma\log\left\{\frac{K}{K^{**}}\right\} = 0,$$

$$(2.3.41)\quad D\log\left\{\frac{K}{K^{**}}\right\} - \frac{b}{1-a}\log\left\{\frac{p}{p^{**}}\right\} = 0,$$

whose solutions, for $\log p$, is

$$(2.3.42)\quad \log p = \log p^{**} + B_1 e^{x_1 t} + B_2 e^{x_2 t}$$

where

$$B_1 = \frac{1}{x_2 - x_1}\left[\left\{x_2 + \frac{\gamma a}{1-a} + \gamma g\right\}\log\left\{\frac{p(0)}{p^{**}(0)}\right\} + \gamma\log\left\{\frac{K(0)}{K^{**}(0)}\right\}\right],$$

$$B_2 = \frac{1}{x_1 - x_2}\left[\left\{x_1 + \frac{\gamma a}{1-a} + \gamma g\right\}\log\left\{\frac{p(0)}{p^{**}(0)}\right\} + \gamma\log\left\{\frac{K(0)}{K^{**}(0)}\right\}\right],$$

and x_1 and x_2 are the roots of (2.3.35). By using (2.3.41), (2.3.42) and (2.3.15) to (2.3.17) we can obtain $K(t)$, $X(t)$, $Q(t)$ and $L(t)$.

2.4 An Alternative Adjustment Process

In each of the models discussed in the preceding sections the rate of increase in the price of the product is related directly to the excess demand for it, while the output is related to the price. But, for an industry in which the condition of perfect competition is only approximately satisfied, it is, perhaps, more realistic to assume that the rate of increase in output is related directly to the excess demand. We now incorporate this alternative assumption in the last model by replacing (2.3.12) by

$$(2.4.1)\quad \frac{DQ}{Q} = \lambda\log\left\{\frac{X}{Q}\right\},$$

which implies that the proportional rate of increase in output is an increasing function of the proportional excess demand.

When considered in conjunction with (2.4.1), equation (2.3.9) is best regarded as a price-determining equation and written in the form

$$(2.4.2)\quad p = \left\{\frac{1}{A}\right\}^{\frac{1}{a}}\left\{\frac{Q}{K}\right\}^{\frac{1-a}{a}}\frac{w}{a}.$$

The interpretation of (2.4.2) is that the price equals the *short-run marginal cost*, which is defined as the cost of producing a small additional unit when the amount of fixed capital is held constant, or, more precisely, as $w\left\{\frac{\partial L}{\partial Q}\right\}$. Equations (2.4.1) and (2.4.2) together imply that, when sales exceeds production firms will be increasing output and, at the same time, increasing the price to the extent necessary to cover the resulting increase in short-run marginal cost.

The complete model now comprises equations (2.3.6), (2.3.8), (2.3.10), (2.3.11), (2.4.1) and (2.4.2). The formal difference between this and the previous model can be seen more clearly in the equation

$$\text{(2.4.3)} \qquad \frac{Dp}{p} = \frac{\lambda(1-a)}{a} \log\left\{\frac{X}{Q}\right\} + \frac{Dw}{w} - \left\{\frac{1-a}{a}\right\}\frac{DK}{K},$$

which follows from (2.4.1) and (2.4.2). Thus, in the revised model, the proportional rate of increase in the price is a function of, not only the proportional excess demand but also the proportional rate of increase in the wage rate and the proportional rate of increase in the amount of fixed capital.

The paths of the endogenous variables for given assumptions about the behaviour of the exogenous variables can be derived as in the previous section. Here we shall consider only the general dynamic properties of the model. We may assume, for this purpose, that the exogenous variables are constant. Then, since, when $Dp = DQ = 0$, equations (2.3.12) and (2.4.1) are identical, the equilibrium values of p, K, L and Q are again given by equations (2.3.22) to (2.3.25). Moreover, from (2.3.16), (2.3.17) and (2.4.3) we obtain

$$\text{(2.4.4)} \quad \left[D + \lambda\left\{1 + \frac{g(1-a)}{a}\right\}\right] \log p + \frac{1-a}{a}(D+\lambda) \log K$$
$$= \lambda \log w + \frac{\lambda(1-a)}{a}\{f \log Y + (g-f) \log p_0\}$$
$$- \frac{\lambda}{a}(\log A + a \log a) + \frac{\lambda(1-a)}{a} \log B,$$

and hence

$$\text{(2.4.5)} \quad \left[D + \lambda\left\{1 + \frac{g(1-a)}{a}\right\}\right] \log\left\{\frac{p}{p^*}\right\} +$$
$$\frac{1-a}{a}(D+\lambda) \log\left\{\frac{K}{K^*}\right\} = 0.$$

And from (2.3.32), which is not affected by the change in assumptions, we have

$$\text{(2.4.6)} \qquad \log\left\{\frac{p}{p^*}\right\} = \frac{1-a}{b} D \log\left\{\frac{K}{K^*}\right\}.$$

Then, from (2.4.5) and (2.4.6) we obtain

$$(2.4.7)\qquad \left[D^2 + \lambda\left\{1 + \frac{g(1-a)}{a} + \frac{b}{\lambda a}\right\}D + \frac{\lambda b}{a}\right]\log\left\{\frac{K}{K^*}\right\} = 0.$$

Since the coefficients in (2.4.7) are all positive the system is stable. And, since

$$(2.4.8)\qquad \lambda^2\left\{1 + \frac{g(1-a)}{a} + \frac{b}{\lambda a}\right\}^2 - \frac{4\lambda b}{a} > \left(\lambda - \frac{b}{a}\right)^2 > 0,$$

oscillations cannot occur. Hence, if the exogenous variables are constant, the endogenous variables converge steadily to their equilibrium values.

We have assumed, so far, that the industry is highly competitive, so that each firm's share of the market is very sensitive to small variations in the price of its product relative to the prices of the products of the other firms in the industry. But the model under discussion can easily be adjusted to allow for imperfect competition by replacing the pricing equation (2.4.2) by

$$(2.4.9)\qquad p = (1+\pi)\left\{\frac{1}{A}\right\}^{\frac{1}{a}}\left\{\frac{Q}{K}\right\}^{\frac{1-a}{a}}\frac{w}{a},$$

in which π is a parameter measuring the degree of imperfection of competition. This adjustment will affect the equilibrium values of the variables, but not the dynamic behaviour of the proportional deviations from equilibrium.

In order to give a more precise interpretation of π, suppose that firm i believes that, when the prices of its competitors' products are constant, its sales will be related to the price of its product by the relation

$$(2.4.10)\qquad X_i = lp_i^{-\epsilon}.$$

The constant, $-\epsilon$, is the estimate by firm i of the price elasticity of demand for its product when other firms hold the prices of their products constant. As $\epsilon \rightarrow \infty$, we approach the state of perfect competition. The coefficient l depends, of course, on the prices of the products of the competing firms, the prices of all other consumers' goods in the market and income. Suppose also that, when the amount of fixed capital is constant, the amount of labour employed by firm i is related to its output by the equation

$$(2.4.11)\qquad L_i = F(Q_i),$$

where F denotes a function which depends on the amount of fixed capital and for which $F' > 0$ and $F'' > 0$. The condition for maximum profit subject to the constraint that sales equal output is

$$\frac{d}{dp_i}\{p_i l p_i^{-\epsilon} - wF(lp_i^{-\epsilon})\} = 0, \tag{2.4.12}$$

which implies that

$$p_i = \frac{\epsilon w}{\epsilon - 1} F'(lp_i^{-\epsilon}). \tag{2.4.13}$$

Hence the parameter π in (2.4.9) can be interpreted as $\frac{1}{\epsilon - 1}$, where $-\epsilon$ is the estimate, by each firm in the industry, of the price elasticity of demand for its product when the other firms hold the prices of their products constant.

CHAPTER 3

MODELS OF THE TRADE CYCLE

VARIATIONS in the total output of an economy should, ideally, be explained by a multi-sector model in which the output, sales and price of each good occur as separate variables and their paths are jointly determined by a single system of equations. Both the theoretical analysis and practical application of such models is still in the early stages, however, and further discussion of them will be postponed until Chapter 8. The next five chapters will be concerned with macro-economic models, or models comprising systems of equations relating aggregate variables such as the national income or output, aggregate consumption and the general price level. In this chapter we shall be concerned with models that are designed to explain and predict short term fluctuations in these variables.

3.1 A Basic Linear Model

We start with a basic linear model which is due to Phillips (1954). The model is

(3.1.1) $$C = (1 - s)Y + A,$$

(3.1.2) $$DK = \gamma(vY - K),$$

(3.1.3) $$DY = \lambda(C + DK - Y),$$

where
$Y =$ real net income or output,
$C =$ real consumption,
$K =$ amount of fixed capital,
$A, s, v, \gamma, \lambda =$ positive constants, $(s < 1)$.

Before discussing the equations we must clarify the meaning of the variables. Y can be interpreted in two ways. First, it is the sum of all incomes derived in the economy divided by an index of prices. Secondly, it can be obtained by subtracting from the *real gross national product* a quantity R (replacement) equal to the output required in order to maintain the existing amount of fixed capital. The real gross national product is the total value of goods and services produced in the economy divided by an index of prices. By constructing a consolidated account of the transactions of all firms in the economy it can be shown that the above two quantities are equal. C is the total expenditure on consumers' goods by final buyers in the economy divided by an index of prices. The meaning of K is similar to that of the K used in section 2.3, except that it now relates to a whole economy. In practice, it is necessary to construct a measure of K by dividing the expenditure on capital goods in each year or quarter by an index of prices, subtracting depreciation and summing the resulting series.

Equation (3.1.1) assumes that real consumption is a linear function of real income or, equivalently, that real saving, $Y–C$ is a linear function of real income. The parameter s equals the proportion of an increment in real income that is saved and is known as the *marginal propensity to save*. The parameter, A, equals that part of real consumption that is independent of income and is known as *autonomous consumption*.

Equation (3.1.2) can be interpreted in several different ways. First we have the direct interpretation that, for any given output Y, there is a certain amount of fixed capital vY that is, in some sense, optimal, and that the rate of investment in fixed capital is proportional to the excess of the optimal amount over the actual amount. The optimum capital–output ratio v can be interpreted as the capital–output ratio at which the marginal rate of substitution of labour for capital equals the ratio of the wage rate to the cost of employing a unit of capital. Since capital is a stock while output is a flow, v is inversely proportional to the unit of time. For example, if time is measured in months, v will be twelve times as great as it would be if time were measured in years.

A second interpretation is that the fundamental investment relation is

$$\frac{DK}{K} = \gamma\left\{\frac{P}{(1 + c)rK} - 1\right\}, \tag{3.1.4}$$

where P denotes real profit, r the interest rate and c a risk premium. Then, if P is a fixed proportion of Y, and v is the ratio of this proportion to $(1 + c)r$, (3.1.4) implies (3.1.2).

A third interpretation (see Phillips (1954)) is that investment in fixed capital depends, with a *distributed time-lag*, on the rate of increase in output. Such a relation is known as an *accelerator* relation and can be written in the form

$$DK = \int_0^\infty w(r)vDQ(t - r)\,dr, \tag{3.1.5}$$

where v denotes the optimum capital–output ratio and $w(r)$ is a non-negative function, for which $\int_0^\infty w(r)\,dr = 1$. In the special case in which $w(r) = \gamma e^{-\gamma r}$ we have

$$\begin{aligned} DK &= \gamma v\int_0^\infty e^{-\gamma r}DQ(t - r)\,dr \\ &= \gamma v\int_{-\infty}^t e^{-\gamma(t-r)}Q'(r)\,dr \\ &= \gamma ve^{-\gamma t}\int_{-\infty}^t e^{\gamma r}Q'(r)\,dr, \end{aligned} \tag{3.1.6}$$

and hence

$$D^2K = \gamma(vDQ - DK). \tag{3.1.7}$$

Integrating (3.1.7) we obtain

$$DK = \gamma(vQ - K) + k, \tag{3.1.8}$$

where k is an arbitrary constant. When $k = 0$, (3.1.2) and (3.1.8) are identical. Although the form of accelerator relation used by Phillips can, as we have shown, be interpreted in several ways, simpler and perhaps less realistic forms of accelerator relation, such as those used in the trade-cycle models of Samuelson (1939) and Hicks (1950), cannot be so interpreted.

Equation (3.1.3) is similar to equation (2.4.1) except that it relates to a whole economy. For $C + DK + R$ equals the total sales of consumers' goods and capital goods to final buyers by all firms in the economy, while $Y + R$ equals the gross output of the economy. Equation (3.1.3) assumes, therefore, that the rate of increase in net output is proportional to the excess of sales over gross output.

The equilibrium values of Y, C and K are given by

$$Y^* = C^* = \frac{A}{s}, \tag{3.1.9}$$

$$K^* = \frac{vA}{s}. \tag{3.1.10}$$

Equations (3.1.9) and (3.1.10) imply that the equilibrium output and equilibrium amount of fixed capital are inversely proportional to the marginal propensity to save. This somewhat surprising result is a consequence of the fact that the model takes no account of the physical limitations on output determined by the size of the labour force and the amount of fixed capital. These limitations will be taken into account in Chapters 4 and 5. Throughout this chapter we implicitly assume that the equilibrium output is less than the output that could be obtained by combining the total labour force with the equilibrium amount of fixed capital. Thus we assume that the equilibrium output is associated with some unemployment and that variations in output are associated with fluctuations in the level of unemployment. The stimulus to the construction of models involving equilibrium with unemployment was provided by Keynes (1936) who constructed a static model yielding an inverse relation between output and the marginal propensity to save.

We note that, when the system is in equilibrium, consumption equals net output. There is then no saving or investment, and the output of the capital goods industries is just sufficient to maintain the equilibrium amount of fixed capital.

From equations (3.1.1), (3.1.2), (3.1.3), (3.1.9) and (3.1.10) we obtain

$$C - C^* = (1 - s)(Y - Y^*), \tag{3.1.11}$$

$$D(K - K^*) = \gamma\{v(Y - Y^*) - (K - K^*)\}, \tag{3.1.12}$$

$$D(Y - Y^*) = \lambda\{(C - C^*) + D(K - K^*) - (Y - Y^*)\}. \tag{3.1.13}$$

Eliminating $C - C^*$ and $D(K - K^*)$ from equations (3.1.11) to (3.1.13) we obtain

$$K - K^* = \left(v - \frac{s}{\gamma}\right)(Y - Y^*) - \frac{1}{\gamma\lambda}D(Y - Y^*) \tag{3.1.14}$$

and hence

$$D(K - K^*) = \left(v - \frac{s}{\gamma}\right)D(Y - Y^*) - \frac{1}{\gamma\lambda}D^2(Y - Y^*). \tag{3.1.15}$$

Then from (3.1.12), (3.1.14) and (3.1.15) we obtain

$$\{D^2 + (\gamma - \gamma\lambda v + \lambda s)D + \gamma\lambda s\}(Y - Y^*) = 0, \tag{3.1.16}$$

whose solution is

$$Y = Y^* + B_1 e^{x_1 t} + B_2 e^{x_2 t} \tag{3.1.17}$$

where

$$B_1 = \frac{1}{x_2 - x_1}[(x_2 + \lambda s - \gamma\lambda v)\{Y(0) - Y^*\} + \gamma\lambda\{K(0) - K^*\}],$$

$$B_2 = \frac{1}{x_1 - x_2}[(x_1 + \lambda s - \gamma\lambda v)\{Y(0) - Y^*\} + \gamma\lambda\{K(0) - K^*\}],$$

and x_1 and x_2 are the roots of

$$x^2 + (\gamma - \gamma\lambda v + \lambda s)x + \gamma\lambda s = 0. \tag{3.1.18}$$

Since $\gamma\lambda s > 0$, a necessary and sufficient condition for the roots of (3.1.18) to have negative real parts is

$$\gamma - \gamma\lambda v + \lambda s > 0, \tag{3.1.19}$$

which implies that

$$v < \frac{1}{\lambda} + \frac{s}{\gamma}. \tag{3.1.20}$$

And a necessary and sufficient condition for complex roots is

$$(\gamma - \gamma\lambda v + \lambda s)^2 < 4\gamma\lambda s, \tag{3.1.21}$$

which implies that

$$v^2 - 2\left(\frac{1}{\lambda} + \frac{s}{\gamma}\right)v + \left(\frac{s}{\gamma} - \frac{1}{\lambda}\right)^2 < 0. \tag{3.1.22}$$

A necessary and sufficient condition for (3.1.22) is that v lies between the roots of the quadratic equation obtained by equating the left-hand side of (3.1.22) to zero. The condition is, therefore, that

$$\left\{\sqrt{\frac{1}{\lambda}}-\sqrt{\frac{s}{\gamma}}\right\}^2 < v < \left\{\sqrt{\frac{1}{\lambda}}+\sqrt{\frac{s}{\gamma}}\right\}^2 \qquad (3.1.23)$$

By combining the conditions (3.1.20) and (3.1.23) we obtain the following table:

Value of v	Path of Y
$v < \left\{\sqrt{\frac{1}{\lambda}}-\sqrt{\frac{s}{\gamma}}\right\}^2$	Non-oscillatory, damped
$\left\{\sqrt{\frac{1}{\lambda}}-\sqrt{\frac{s}{\gamma}}\right\}^2 < v < \frac{1}{\lambda}+\frac{s}{\gamma}$	Oscillatory, damped
$\frac{1}{\lambda}+\frac{s}{\gamma} < v < \left\{\sqrt{\frac{1}{\lambda}}+\sqrt{\frac{s}{\gamma}}\right\}^2$	Oscillatory, explosive
$\left\{\sqrt{\frac{1}{\lambda}}+\sqrt{\frac{s}{\gamma}}\right\}^2 < v$	Non-oscillatory, explosive

We note that the type of path followed by Y is not affected by an equal proportional change in v, $\frac{1}{\lambda}$ and $\frac{1}{\gamma}$. This is as we should expect. For each of these parameters is inversely proportional to the unit of time. Allen (1959) suggested that the above model is likely to yield a damped path only if $\gamma > \lambda$. But it is clear from the above table that, for any given values of v, s and $\frac{\gamma}{\lambda}$, the path will be damped if γ and λ are sufficiently small, and explosive if γ and λ are sufficiently large.

There is fairly general agreement, among economists, that modern industrial economies tend to generate cyclical fluctuations in output and employment, with an average period of about 8 years between peaks. Such fluctuations are known as the *trade cycle*. The above model is consistent with two alternative explanations of this cycle. The first is that the system generates damped oscillations which are prevented from dying out by disturbances such as wars, inventions and variations in the weather. This explanation corresponds to the case in which $\left\{\sqrt{\frac{1}{\lambda}}-\sqrt{\frac{s}{\gamma}}\right\}^2 < v < \frac{1}{\lambda}+\frac{s}{\gamma}$, provided that a disturbance is introduced into each equation.

The second explanation is that the system generates explosive oscillations which are constrained by the productive capacity of the economy. This explanation corresponds to the case in which $\frac{1}{\lambda}+\frac{s}{\gamma} < v < \left\{\sqrt{\frac{1}{\lambda}}+\sqrt{\frac{s}{\gamma}}\right\}^2$. Equation (3.1.3) is assumed to hold only when $Y < f(L_s, K)$, where f denotes a production function and L_s the labour supply. Otherwise, we assume that $Y = f(L_s, K)$. Hence, if $\frac{1}{\lambda} + \frac{s}{\gamma} < v < \left\{\sqrt{\frac{1}{\lambda}} + \sqrt{\frac{s}{\gamma}}\right\}^2$, the path of each variable will converge to a limit cycle, alternate phases of which are determined by the systems comprising (3.1.1), (3.1.2) and either (3.1.3) or $Y = f(L_s, K)$.

Casual observation of the unemployment statistics of the United Kingdom and United States suggests that the first explanation is more likely to be correct. If so, the realism of the model can be checked by considering whether or not there are plausible values of the parameters satisfying $\left\{\sqrt{\frac{1}{\lambda}} - \sqrt{\frac{s}{\gamma}}\right\}^2 < v < \frac{1}{\lambda} + \frac{s}{\gamma}$. This check will be facilitated by a reinterpretation of γ and λ.

Equation (3.1.2) is satisfied by

$$K = \gamma v \int_0^\infty e^{-\gamma r} Q(t - r)\, dr. \qquad (3.1.24)$$

The interpretation of (3.1.24) is that the amount of fixed capital depends, with a distributed time-lag, on output. Now $\frac{1}{\gamma} = \int_0^\infty r\gamma e^{-\gamma r} dr$ which can be interpreted as the mean time-lag between a change in output and the induced change in the amount of fixed capital. Suppose, for example, that at time zero, we have $K = vQ$ and that Q suddenly increases by a million units and thereafter remains constant. Then, over the infinite future, K will increase by v million units and $\frac{1}{\gamma}$ is the mean of the times at which the different units will appear. Alternatively, since $\int_0^{1/\gamma} \gamma e^{-\gamma r} dr = 0{\cdot}632$, $\frac{1}{\gamma}$ can be interpreted as the time required for 63·2 per cent of the induced increment in fixed capital to appear. The parameter λ can be interpreted similarly, except that $\frac{1}{\lambda}$ is a measure of the time-lag in the adjustment of output to sales. We shall refer to a parameter such as γ or λ as the *speed of response* and its reciprocal as the *mean time-lag*.

A comparison of the estimate by Redfern (1955) of the fixed capital in the United Kingdom with the official estimate of the national income suggests a plausible value of v of at least 2·0 when the unit of time is taken as a year. Assuming that the mean time-lag in the adjustment of fixed capital to output is not greater than 3 years, the mean time-lag in the adjustment of output to sales not greater than 6 months and the marginal propensity to save not greater than 0·3, we have $\frac{1}{\lambda} + \frac{s}{\gamma} \leq 1{\cdot}4$

and $\left\{\sqrt{\frac{1}{\lambda}} + \sqrt{\frac{s}{\gamma}}\right\}^2 \leq 2{\cdot}7$. If, in addition, $v > 1{\cdot}4$ the path of Y will be explosive, while if $v > 2{\cdot}7$ it will be both explosive and non-oscillatory.

The above calculations, perhaps, cast some doubt on the direct usefulness of the simple model discussed in this section. The model may, nevertheless, provide a useful basis for the construction of more realistic models. It will be developed in various ways in the following sections.

3.2 A Lag in the Consumption Relation

Perhaps the most unrealistic feature of the model discussed in the previous section is the assumption that consumption responds instantaneously to a change in income. We now replace (3.1.1) by

$$DC = \alpha\{(1 - s)Y + A - C\}, \tag{3.2.1}$$

in which α is a speed of response parameter. Equation (3.2.1) has the direct interpretation that, associated with any given level of income, there is a desired level of consumption, $(1 - s)Y + A$, and that the rate of increase in consumption is proportional to the excess of the desired level over the actual level. Alternatively, it can be regarded as a transformation of

$$C = (1 - s)\alpha\int_0^{\infty} e^{-\alpha r}\, Y(t - r)dr + A, \tag{3.2.2}$$

which implies that consumption depends on income at all previous points of time, with less weight being attached to income in the more remote past. One interpretation of (3.2.2) is that consumption depends on the present value of expected future income and that expectations concerning future income are based on past income (see Friedman (1957)).

The complete model now comprises equations (3.2.1), (3.1.2) and (3.1.3). The equilibrium values of C, Y and K are again given by (3.1.9) and (3.1.10). And from (3.2.1), (3.1.2), (3.1.3), (3.1.9) and (3.1.10) we obtain

$$Dy = Fy \tag{3.2.3}$$

where

$$y = \begin{bmatrix} C - C^* \\ K - K^* \\ Y - Y^* \end{bmatrix}$$

$$F = \begin{bmatrix} -\alpha & 0 & \alpha(1 - s) \\ 0 & -\gamma & \gamma v \\ \lambda & -\gamma\lambda & -\lambda(1 - \gamma v) \end{bmatrix}.$$

Now let H be a matrix whose rows are characteristic vectors of F so that

$$HFH^{-1} = \begin{bmatrix} x_1 & 0 & 0 \\ 0 & x_2 & 0 \\ 0 & 0 & x_3 \end{bmatrix}, \tag{3.2.4}$$

where the x_i's are the characteristic roots (which we assume to be distinct) of F. Then, since $D(Hy) = (HFH^{-1})Hy$ we have

$$y = H^{-1} \begin{bmatrix} e^{x_1 t} & 0 & 0 \\ 0 & e^{x_2 t} & 0 \\ 0 & 0 & e^{x_3 t} \end{bmatrix} Hy(0). \tag{3.2.5}$$

Using (3.2.5) we can express each of the variables C, K and Y as a function of t, $C(0)$, $K(0)$ and $Y(0)$.

The characteristic roots of F are the roots of

$$x^3 + a_1 x^2 + a_2 x + a_3 = 0, \tag{3.2.6}$$

where

$$\begin{aligned} a_1 &= \alpha + \gamma + \lambda - \gamma\lambda v, \\ a_2 &= \alpha\gamma + \gamma\lambda + \alpha\lambda s - \alpha\gamma\lambda v, \\ a_3 &= \alpha\gamma\lambda s. \end{aligned}$$

Necessary and sufficient conditions for these roots to have negative real parts are

$$\begin{aligned} a_1 &> 0, \\ a_3 &> 0, \\ a_1 a_2 - a_3 &> 0. \end{aligned}$$

These follow from the Routh–Hurwitz conditions (see Gantmacher (1959)) for the roots of $\sum_{i=0}^{n} a_i z^{n-i} = 0$ to have negative real parts. If $a_0 > 0$, the latter conditions are

$$a_1 > 0, \begin{vmatrix} a_1 & a_3 \\ a_0 & a_2 \end{vmatrix} > 0, \begin{vmatrix} a_1 & a_3 & a_5 \\ a_0 & a_2 & a_4 \\ 0 & a_1 & a_3 \end{vmatrix} > 0, \ldots$$

$$\ldots \begin{vmatrix} a_1 & a_3 & a_5 & \cdot & \cdot & \cdot & 0 \\ a_0 & a_2 & a_4 & \cdot & \cdot & \cdot & 0 \\ 0 & a_1 & a_3 & \cdot & \cdot & \cdot & 0 \\ 0 & a_0 & a_2 & \cdot & \cdot & \cdot & 0 \\ \cdot & \cdot & \cdot & \cdot & \cdot & \cdot & \cdot \\ \cdot & \cdot & \cdot & \cdot & \cdot & \cdot & a_n \end{vmatrix} > 0.$$

Suppose, for example, that $v = 2{\cdot}0$, $s = 0{\cdot}25$, $\gamma = 0{\cdot}4$ and $\lambda = 4{\cdot}0$. Then it follows from the above conditions that a necessary and sufficient condition for stability is $\alpha < 0{\cdot}8$. More generally it can be seen that the system will always be stable if $v < \frac{1}{\gamma} + \frac{1}{\lambda}$ and α is sufficiently small. Thus, for plausible values of v, γ and λ, a time-lag in the consumption relation has a stabilising influence. Moreover, for the above values of

v, s, γ and λ and all values of α in the stable region, two of the roots of (3.2.6) are complex so that the paths of the variables are oscillatory.

The model discussed in section 3.1 can be regarded as the limiting case of the above model when α tends to infinity. For the above values of v, s, γ and λ it yields a path of Y that is both explosive and non-oscillatory.

3.3 The Influence of Stocks

Another way in which the basic model can be made more realistic is by allowing for the influence of stocks in the output adjustment process. This can be done by replacing (3.1.3) by

$$DY = \lambda(C + DK - Y) + \mu(S^0 - S), \tag{3.3.1}$$

$$S^0 = b(C + DK) + c, \tag{3.3.2}$$

$$DS = Y - C - DK, \tag{3.3.3}$$

in which S^0 and S denote the desired and actual stock levels respectively and μ, b and c are positive constants. S includes stocks of both consumers' goods and capital goods. It includes, for example, building materials that have not yet been incorporated in buildings and machines that have not yet been sold to final buyers. Equation (3.3.1) assumes that the rate of increase in output is greater, the greater is the excess of sales over output and the greater the excess of desired stocks over actual stocks. The parameter $\frac{1}{\mu}$ can be interpreted as the mean time-lag in the adjustment of stocks to sales.

The complete model now comprises equations (3.1.2), (3.2.1), (3.3.1), (3.3.2) and (3.3.3), and determines the paths of C, Y, K, S and S^0. The equilibrium values of C, Y and K are given by (3.1.9) and (3.1.10) and the equilibrium values of S and S^0 by

$$S^* = S^{0*} = \frac{bA}{s} + c. \tag{3.3.4}$$

From (3.1.2), (3.2.1), (3.3.1), (3.3.2), (3.3.3), (3.1.9), (3.1.10) and (3.3.4) we obtain, after eliminating S^0, the system

$$Dy = Fy, \tag{3.3.5}$$

where

$$y = \begin{bmatrix} C - C^* \\ K - K^* \\ Y - Y^* \\ S - S^* \end{bmatrix}$$

$$F = \begin{bmatrix} -\alpha & 0 & \alpha(1 - s) & 0 \\ 0 & -\gamma & \gamma v & 0 \\ \lambda + \mu b & -(\gamma\lambda + \mu b\gamma) & \mu b\gamma v - \lambda(1 - \gamma v) & -\mu \\ -1 & \gamma & 1 - \gamma v & 0 \end{bmatrix}$$

The solution of (3.3.5) can be expressed in a form similar to (3.2.5), so that each of the variables C, K, Y and S can be expressed as a function of t, $C(0)$, $K(0)$, $Y(0)$ and $S(0)$.

The characteristic roots of F are the roots of

$$x^4 + a_1x^3 + a_2x^2 + a_3x + a_4 = 0, \tag{3.3.6}$$

where

$$\begin{aligned} a_1 &= \alpha + \gamma + \lambda - \gamma\lambda v - \mu b\gamma v, \\ a_2 &= \alpha\gamma + \gamma\lambda + \alpha s\lambda - \alpha\gamma\lambda v + \mu(1 - \alpha b - \gamma v + \alpha s b - \alpha b\gamma v), \\ a_3 &= \alpha\gamma\lambda s + \mu(\gamma + \alpha s - \alpha\gamma b - \alpha\gamma v + \alpha\gamma b s), \\ a_4 &= \mu\alpha\gamma s. \end{aligned}$$

Necessary and sufficient conditions for these roots to have negative real parts are

$$\begin{aligned} a_1 &> 0, \\ a_4 &> 0, \\ a_1a_2 - a_3 &> 0, \\ a_1a_2a_3 - a_3^2 - a_1^2a_4 &> 0. \end{aligned}$$

We note that at least one of these conditions (i.e. the first) will not be satisfied if μ is sufficiently large. The system will be unstable, therefore, if the influence of stocks on the rate of change of output is sufficiently strong.

Suppose, for example, that $\alpha = 0{\cdot}6$, $\gamma = 0{\cdot}4$, $\lambda = 4{\cdot}0$, $s = 0{\cdot}25$ and $v = 2{\cdot}0$. Under these assumptions the path of Y generated by the model discussed in section 3.2 is damped and oscillatory. If we assume, also, that $b = 0{\cdot}5$, which is the approximate ratio of stocks to the gross national product in the United Kingdom, then a necessary and sufficient condition for stability, in the model under discussion, is that $\mu < 0{\cdot}6$. For any value of μ in this range and the above values of the other parameters, equation (3.3.6) has two complex and two real roots.

3.4 Government Transactions and Foreign Trade

As a final extension of the basic linear model we shall construct a model incorporating imports, exports, taxation and government expenditure. The model is

$$DC = \alpha\{(1 - s)(Y - T) + A - C\}, \tag{3.4.1}$$

$$DK = \gamma(vY - K), \tag{3.4.2}$$

$$DY = \lambda(C + DK + G + E - I - Y) + \mu(S^0 - S), \tag{3.4.3}$$

$$S^0 = b(C + DK + G + E) + c, \tag{3.4.4}$$

$$DS = Y + I - E - G - C - DK, \tag{3.4.5}$$

$$I = m(C + DK + G + E), \tag{3.4.6}$$

$$T = \tau Y - B, \tag{3.4.7}$$

where $Y =$ real net income or output,
$C =$ real private consumption,
$K =$ private fixed capital,
$S =$ actual stocks,
$S^0 =$ desired stocks,
$I =$ real imports,
$T =$ real taxation minus real government transfers,
$E =$ real exports,
$G =$ real government expenditure on goods and services,

$s, v, b, c, m, \alpha, \gamma, \lambda, \tau, \mu, A, B =$ positive constants, $(s, m, \tau < 1)$.

The variables E and G are assumed to be exogenous.

Equation (3.4.1) differs from (3.2.1) only in that Y is replaced by $Y - T$. The variable T equals real taxation (i.e. taxation in money units divided by an index of prices) minus real government transfers such as pensions. The latter can be regarded as negative taxation for the purpose of economic analysis. $Y - T$ is the amount available for private consumption and saving and is known as *real disposable income*. C equals the total real expenditure by private consumers on both home produced and imported consumers' goods.

Equation (3.4.2) is formally identical with (3.1.2). It should be noted, however, that DK is the rate of increase in private fixed capital only. Government fixed capital formation is now included in G, which we have assumed to be exogenous.

Equation (3.4.3) is similar to (3.3.1). But the total sales by firms in the economy is now made up of four components: (1) sales of consumers' goods to individual consumers in the economy, (2) sales of capital goods to firms in the economy, (3) sales to the government, (4) sales to foreign buyers. After subtracting imports we have the net sales to be met from home production. Finally, we obtain the term $C + DK + G + E - I - Y$ which is the excess of net sales over output.

Equation (3.4.4) assumes that the desired stock level is a linear function of gross sales, and equation (3.4.6) that imports are a constant proportion of gross sales. Equation (3.4.7) could be deduced from the assumption that both real taxation and real government transfers are linear functions of real income. The negative constant $-B$ implies that $\frac{T}{Y}$ is an increasing function of Y.

The equilibrium values of the variables are given by

$$(3.4.8) \qquad Y^* = \frac{(1-m)(E+G+A)+(1-m)(1-s)B}{1-(1-m)(1-s)(1-\tau)},$$

$$(3.4.9) \qquad C^* = \frac{(1-m)(1-s)(1-\tau)(E+G)+A+(1-s)B}{1-(1-m)(1-s)(1-\tau)},$$

(3.4.10) $$I^* = \frac{m\{E + G + A + (1 - s)B\}}{1 - (1 - m)(1 - s)(1 - \tau)},$$

(3.4.11) $$T^* = \frac{\tau(1 - m)(E + G + A) - \{1 - (1 - m)(1 - s)\}B}{1 - (1 - m)(1 - s)(1 - \tau)},$$

(3.4.12) $$K^* = \frac{v\{(1 - m)(E + G + A) + (1 - m)(1 - s)B\}}{1 - (1 - m)(1 - s)(1 - \tau)},$$

(3.4.13) $$S^* = \frac{b\{E + G + A + (1 - s)B\}}{1 - (1 - m)(1 - s)(1 - \tau)} + c.$$

It is evident from (3.4.8) that Y^* will be greater, the greater are G, E, A and B, and the smaller are s, m and τ. The explanation of this is that government expenditure, exports and autonomous private consumption are associated with new injections into the circular flow of money, while saving, imports and taxation are associated with leakages from this flow. The equilibrium level of income is such that the leakages equal the injections.

From equations (3.4.1) to (3.4.13) we obtain, after eliminating S^0, I and T, the system

(3.4.14) $$Dy = Fy,$$

where

$$y = \begin{bmatrix} C - C^* \\ K - K^* \\ Y - Y^* \\ S - S^* \end{bmatrix}$$

$$F = \begin{bmatrix} -\alpha & 0 & \alpha(1 - s)(1 - \tau) & 0 \\ 0 & -\gamma & \gamma v & 0 \\ \lambda(1 - m) + \mu b & -\gamma\lambda(1 - m) - \mu b\gamma & v\gamma\lambda(1 - m) - \lambda + \mu b\gamma v & -\mu \\ -(1 - m) & \gamma(1 - m) & 1 - \gamma v(1 - m) & 0 \end{bmatrix}$$

The characteristic roots of F are the roots of

(3.4.15) $$x^4 + a_1x^3 + a_2x^2 + a_3x + a_4 = 0,$$

where $$a_1 = \alpha + \gamma + \lambda - \gamma\lambda v(1 - m) - \mu b\gamma v,$$

$$a_2 = \alpha\gamma + \gamma\lambda + \alpha\lambda\{1 - (1 - m)(1 - s)(1 - \tau)\} - \alpha\gamma\lambda v(1 - m) + \mu\{1 - \alpha b(1 - s)(1 - \tau) - \gamma v(1 - m) - \alpha b\gamma v\},$$

$$a_3 = \alpha\gamma\lambda\{1 - (1 - m)(1 - s)(1 - \tau)\} + \mu[\gamma + \alpha\{1 - (1 - m)(1 - s)(1 - \tau)\} - \alpha\gamma b(1 - s)(1 - \tau) - \alpha\gamma v(1 - m)],$$

$$a_4 = \mu\alpha\gamma\{1 - (1 - m)(1 - s)(1 - \tau)\}.$$

It is evident from the table in section 3.1 that, in the basic model, an increase in the marginal propensity to save has a stabilising effect. This is the normal effect in the more complicated models also. The effect of leakages through taxation and imports are similar. Suppose, for example, that α, γ, λ, s, v and b have the values assumed in section 3.3, so that, with no taxation or imports, the condition for stability is $\mu < 0{\cdot}6$. If we now assume that $\tau = 0{\cdot}2$ and $m = 0{\cdot}2$, the stability condition is $\mu < 2{\cdot}9$.

As a particular example consider the case in which $\mu = 2{\cdot}0$, so that the mean time-lag in the adjustment of stocks to sales is 6 months. Then the complete list of assumed values of the parameters is: $\alpha = 0{\cdot}60$, $\gamma = 0{\cdot}40$, $\lambda = 4{\cdot}00$, $\mu = 2{\cdot}00$, $s = 0{\cdot}25$, $m = 0{\cdot}20$, $\tau = 0{\cdot}20$, $v = 2{\cdot}00$, $b = 0{\cdot}50$. From (3.4.15) we have

$$(3.4.16) \qquad x^4 + 1{\cdot}64x^3 + 1{\cdot}43x^2 + 1{\cdot}02x + 0{\cdot}24 = 0,$$

whose roots are: $-0{\cdot}35$, $-0{\cdot}99$, $-0{\cdot}15 + (0{\cdot}81)i$, $-0{\cdot}15 - (0{\cdot}81)i$. In this case, therefore, the model generates a damped cycle with a period of about 8 years.

The exogenous variables, E and G have, so far, been treated as constants. But the model could be used for predicting the paths of the endogenous variables corresponding to any assumed paths of the exogenous variables. It could also be used as a basis for the construction of an international model in which both the imports and exports of each country would be treated as endogenous variables. As an example, suppose that there were only two countries, A and B. Then the exports of A would equal the imports of B, and vice versa. The complete model would comprise a set of equations similar to equations (3.4.1) to (3.4.7) for each country. These 14 equations would be sufficient to determine the paths of all the endogenous variables corresponding to any assumed paths of government expenditure in each country.

3.5 A Non-linear Model

The equations of the models discussed in sections 3.1 to 3.4 are best regarded as linear approximations. For there is no reason for expecting the true relations to be linear. There are, indeed, good *a priori* reasons for expecting the second derivatives of the functions in certain relations to be definitely positive or negative. In such cases it is preferable that the approximations should be non-linear.

We shall now construct a non-linear model which emphasises the role of prices and profits in the trade-cycle mechanism. The model is

$$(3.5.1) \qquad C = AY^{a},$$

$$(3.5.2) \qquad \frac{DK}{K} = \gamma \log \left\{ \frac{pY - wL}{(1 + c)rpK} \right\},$$

(3.5.3) $$L = BY^b K^{1-b},$$

(3.5.4) $$p = (1 + \pi)w\frac{\partial L}{\partial Y} = \frac{b(1 + \pi)wL}{Y},$$

(3.5.5) $$DY = \lambda(C + DK - Y),$$

where $Y =$ real net income or output,
$C =$ real consumption,
$K =$ amount of fixed capital,
$L =$ amount of labour employed,
$p =$ price level,
$w =$ wage rate,
$r =$ interest rate,
$A, B, a, b, c, \gamma, \lambda, \pi =$ positive constants ($a < 1, b > 1$).

The variables w and r are assumed to be exogenous.

Equation (3.5.1) assumes, like (3.1.1) that consumption, saving and the proportion of income saved are all increasing functions of income. But it differs from (3.1.1) in that the proportion of the marginal unit of income saved is also assumed to be an increasing function of income.

The term $pY - wL$, in equation (3.5.2), equals profit measured in money units, while pK can be interpreted as the value of fixed capital measured in money units. The term $\frac{pY - wL}{pK}$ can be interpreted, therefore, as the rate of profit on fixed capital. The equation assumes that the proportional rate of investment in fixed capital is an increasing function of the ratio of the rate of profit on fixed capital to the rate of interest. It is similar to equation (2.3.10), except that the variables now relate to a whole economy. The parameter c can, as in (2.3.10), be interpreted as a risk premium.

Equation (3.5.3) is a Cobb–Douglas production relation, between the output of the economy, the amount of labour employed and the amount of fixed capital. But, whereas output is usually expressed as an explicit function of the inputs of labour and capital, as in (2.3.6), here we express the amount of labour employed as an explicit function of output and the amount of fixed capital. For, in view of (3.5.5), the structure of the model is more easily understood if (3.5.3) is thought of as an employment equation.

Equation (3.5.4) assumes that the price level equals the short-run marginal cost of output plus a proportional margin π which depends on the degree of imperfection of competition. It is similar to (2.4.9) except that $\frac{\partial L}{\partial Y}$ is expressed as a function of $\frac{Y}{L}$ rather than $\frac{Y}{K}$. The equation implies that the price level equals the labour cost per unit of output plus a proportional margin, $b(1 + \pi) - 1$. The model is completed by (3.5.5) which is identical with (3.1.3).

Eliminating p and L from (3.5.2), (3.5.3) and (3.5.4) we obtain

$$\frac{DK}{K} = \gamma \log \left[\frac{\{b(1+\pi)-1\}Y}{b(1+\pi)(1+c)rK}\right]. \tag{3.5.6}$$

Then, from (3.5.1), (3.5.5) and (3.5.6) we obtain

$$\log C = a \log Y + \log A, \tag{3.5.7}$$

$$D \log K = \gamma (\log Y - \log K) + \gamma \log \left\{\frac{b(1+\pi)-1}{b(1+\pi)(1+c)r}\right\}, \tag{3.5.8}$$

$$D \log Y = \lambda\left(\frac{C}{Y} + \frac{DK}{Y} - 1\right). \tag{3.5.9}$$

The paths of C, K and Y are determined by their initial values and the system comprising equations (3.5.7) to (3.5.9). This system has a particular solution

$$Y^* = C^* = A^{1/(1-a)}, \tag{3.5.10}$$

$$K^* = \frac{\{b(1+\pi)-1\}A^{1/(1-a)}}{b(1+\pi)(1+c)r}. \tag{3.5.11}$$

As in the basic linear model the equilibrium output, Y^*, depends only on the parameters of the consumption function. The equilibrium amount of fixed capital, K^* is directly proportional to the equilibrium output and inversely proportional to the interest rate.

From (3.5.9) we obtain

$$\begin{aligned} D \log Y &= \lambda\{e^{\log C - \log Y} + (D \log K)e^{\log K - \log Y} - 1\} \\ &= \lambda\{e^{\log A - (1-a)\log Y} + (D \log K)e^{\log K - \log Y} - 1\}. \end{aligned} \tag{3.5.12}$$

Now let y_1 and y_2 denote $\log\left\{\frac{K}{K^*}\right\}$ and $\log\left\{\frac{Y}{Y^*}\right\}$, respectively. Then, from (3.5.8), (3.5.10), (3.5.11) and (3.5.12), we obtain

$$Dy_1 = \gamma(y_2 - y_1), \tag{3.5.13}$$

$$Dy_2 = \lambda\left\{e^{-(1-a)y_2} + \frac{\gamma g}{r}(y_2 - y_1)e^{y_1 - y_2} - 1\right\}, \tag{3.5.14}$$

where

$$g = \frac{b(1+\pi)-1}{b(1+\pi)(1+c)}.$$

And from (3.5.14) we obtain

$$Dy_2 = \lambda\left\{-\frac{\gamma g}{r}y_1 + \left(\frac{\gamma g}{r} + a - 1\right)y_2\right\} + \phi(y_1, y_2), \tag{3.5.15}$$

where $\phi(y_1, y_2) = \frac{\gamma g}{r}(y_2 - y_1)(e^{y_1 - y_2} - 1) + \sum_{i=2}^{\infty} \frac{\{(a-1)y_2\}^i}{i!}$

Moreover, it is clear that $\frac{\phi(y_1, y_2)}{|y_1| + |y_2|}$ tends to zero as y_1 and y_2 tend to zero. Provided, therefore, that the initial values of K and Y do not differ too much from K^* and Y^* we can expect to obtain good predictions of the paths of these variables by solving the linear system

(3.5.16) $$Dy = Fy,$$

where

$$y = \begin{bmatrix} \log (K/K^*) \\ \log (Y/Y^*) \end{bmatrix},$$

$$F = \begin{bmatrix} -\gamma & \gamma \\ -\frac{\gamma\lambda g}{r} & \lambda\left(\frac{\gamma g}{r} + a - 1\right) \end{bmatrix}.$$

It can be shown, in particular, that y_1 and y_2 will tend to zero as $t \longrightarrow \infty$ if the characteristic roots of F have negative real parts and $y_1(0)$ and $y_2(0)$ are sufficiently small (see Struble (1962)). We shall say, in this case, that the system is *locally stable*. But it should be remembered that, even if a system is locally stable, the paths of the variables may be explosive if the initial deviations from equilibrium are sufficiently large. It is also possible for the paths generated by a non-linear system to be bounded even if the system is not locally stable. A trade-cycle model having the latter property was constructed by Goodwin (1951).

A necessary and sufficient condition for the characteristic roots of F to have negative real parts is

(3.5.17) $$\gamma\left(\frac{\lambda g}{r} - 1\right) < \lambda(1 - a).$$

Since $\frac{g}{r}$ is the equilibrium ratio of fixed capital to output and $\frac{1}{\lambda}$ the mean time-lag in the adjustment of output to sales, we may assume that $\frac{\lambda g}{r} > 1$. The condition (3.5.17) is then equivalent to

(3.5.18) $$\gamma < \frac{\lambda(1 - a)}{\frac{\lambda g}{r} - 1}.$$

A necessary and sufficient condition for the characteristic roots of F to be complex is

(3.5.19) $$\left(\gamma + \lambda(1 - a) - \frac{\gamma\lambda g}{r}\right)^2 < 4\gamma\lambda(1 - a),$$

which implies that

(3.5.20) $$\left\{\frac{\sqrt{\lambda g/r} - 1}{\lambda g/r - 1}\right\}^2 < \frac{\gamma}{\lambda(1 - a)} < \left\{\frac{\sqrt{\lambda g/r} + 1}{\lambda g/r - 1}\right\}^2.$$

Suppose, for example, that $\frac{g}{r} = 2{\cdot}0$, $\lambda = 4{\cdot}0$ and $a = 0{\cdot}8$. Then the paths of the variables will be non-oscillatory and damped if $\gamma < 0{\cdot}054$, oscillatory and damped if $0{\cdot}054 < \gamma < 0{\cdot}114$, oscillatory and explosive if $0{\cdot}114 < \gamma < 0{\cdot}239$, and non-oscillatory and explosive if $\gamma > 0{\cdot}239$. The parameter γ is approximately equal to the ratio of the proportional rate of investment in fixed capital to the proportional excess of the actual rate of profit over the rate of profit at which the amount of fixed capital would be held constant. The value of γ required in order for the system to be stable appears, therefore, to be unrealistically low. But the model can be made more realistic by introducing a time-lag in the consumption relation, and, as in the case of the linear model, this has a stabilising influence.

We introduce a time-lag in the consumption relation by replacing (3.5.1) by

$$\text{(3.5.21)} \qquad \frac{DC}{C} = \alpha \log \left\{\frac{AY^a}{C}\right\},$$

which assumes that the proportional rate of increase in consumption is an increasing function of the proportional excess of desired consumption over actual consumption. From (3.5.21) we obtain

$$\text{(3.5.22)} \qquad D \log C = \alpha(a \log Y - \log C + \log A),$$

which replaces (3.5.7). The paths of K, Y and C are now determined by their initial values and equations (3.5.8), (3.5.9) and (3.5.22), and their equilibrium values are, again, given by (3.5.10) and (3.5.11).

From (3.5.10) and (3.5.22) we obtain

$$\text{(3.5.23)} \qquad Dy_3 = \alpha(ay_2 - y_3),$$

where y_3 denotes $\log \left\{\frac{C}{C^*}\right\}$. And, from equations (3.5.9) to (3.5.11) and (3.5.13), we obtain

$$\text{(3.5.24)} \quad Dy_2 = \lambda\left\{e^{y_3 - y_2} + \frac{\gamma g}{r}(y_2 - y_1)e^{y_1 - y_2} - 1\right\},$$

$$= \lambda\left\{y_3 + \left(\frac{\gamma g}{r} - 1\right)y_2 - \frac{\gamma g}{r}y_1\right\} + \psi(y_1, y_2, y_3),$$

where $\frac{\psi(y_1, y_2, y_3)}{|y_1| + |y_2| + |y_3|}$ tends to zero as y_1, y_2 and y_3 tend to zero. The exact paths of the y_i's are determined by their initial values and equations (3.5.13), (3.5.23) and (3.5.24), and the approximate paths by the initial values and the system

$$Dy = Gy, \tag{3.5.25}$$

where
$$G = \begin{bmatrix} -\gamma & \gamma & 0 \\ -\frac{\gamma\lambda g}{r} & \lambda\left(\frac{\gamma g}{r} - 1\right) & \lambda \\ 0 & \alpha a & -\alpha \end{bmatrix}.$$

The system is locally stable if the characteristic roots of G have negative real parts.

The characteristic roots of G are the roots of

$$x^3 + a_1x^2 + a_2x + a_3 = 0, \tag{3.5.26}$$

where
$$a_1 = \alpha + \gamma + \lambda - \frac{\gamma\lambda g}{r},$$

$$a_2 = \alpha\gamma + \gamma\lambda + \alpha\lambda(1 - a) - \frac{\alpha\gamma\lambda g}{r},$$

$$a_3 = \alpha\gamma\lambda(1 - a).$$

If we assume that $\alpha = 1{\cdot}0$ and that λ and $\frac{g}{r}$ have the values assumed above, then the condition for these roots to have negative real parts is $\gamma < 0{\cdot}25$.

We have assumed, so far, that r is constant. But the model could, of course, be used for predicting the paths of the endogenous variables corresponding to any assumed path of r. It could also be developed further by treating r as an endogenous variable. This sort of development will be postponed until Chapter 5. There we shall construct a model in which monetary phenomena play an essential role in the synthesis of cycles and growth.

CHAPTER 4

MODELS OF GROWTH WITH FULL EMPLOYMENT

THE income paths generated by the models discussed in Chapter 3 differ from those relating to most actual economies in that they oscillate about a constant equilibrium value rather than a long-term upward trend. Consequently, these models could not be used for long-term prediction, and they could be used for short-term prediction only by identifying the variables in the model with deviations of the observed variables from their trends. The next step in the development of more realistic models is to introduce the growth mechanism.

In this chapter we shall consider models that assume a continuous state of full employment so that output grows without oscillating. Whereas, in the models discussed in Chapter 3, the variation in output is associated with fluctuations in the level of employment, in the following models it is associated with technical progress, population growth and the accumulation of capital. Since most economies are subject to fluctuations in employment, the models will be of little use for short-term prediction. But they could be used as simple tools for long-term prediction, and, together with the models of Chapter 3, they provide a basis for the construction of more realistic models in Chapter 5.

4.1 A Basic Model

We start with the simple *neo-classical model* which is due to Solow (1956) and Swan (1956). Its basic components are a production function, a consumption function and a labour supply function. The model is characterised by having no explicit investment function. Instead, it is assumed that the path of investment is such as to ensure a continuous state of full employment. We could assume that investment is determined by an equation like (3.5.2). But it would then be assumed that the path of r is such as to preserve full employment.

Although the choice of convenient functional forms is an important part of econometric model construction, it is useful to know which properties of our models are a consequence of the particular functional forms chosen and which will hold under more general assumptions. Initially, therefore, we shall allow the production function to be any member of a class of functions. We shall assume, in particular, that it can be written in the form

$$L = e^{-\rho t}F(Y, K), \tag{4.1.1}$$

where L, Y and K denote the amount of labour employed, real net income or output and the amount of capital respectively, ρ is a positive constant and F denotes a continuous function which has the following properties:

(i) $F(Y, K)$ exists and is positive for all positive vectors (Y, K);
(ii) $F(Y, K)$ is homogeneous of the first degree;
(iii) $\partial F/\partial Y > 0$;
(iv) $\partial F/\partial K < 0$;
(v) $F(Y, K) \longrightarrow \infty$ as $Y \longrightarrow \infty$;
(vi) $F(Y, K) \longrightarrow 0$ as $Y \longrightarrow 0$.

Equation (4.1.1) implies that technical progress is neutral in the sense that the proportional rate of decrease in the amount of labour required in order to produce a given output Y, with a given amount of capital K, is independent of Y and K. Neutrality of technical progress, in this sense, can be contrasted with that implied by a relation of the form

$$Y = e^{\rho t}G(L, K), \tag{4.1.2}$$

where G denotes a function. Equation (4.1.2) implies that technical progress is neutral in the sense that the proportional rate of increase in the output obtained by using a given amount of labour L, in conjunction with a given amount of capital K, is independent of L and K. The concepts of neutral technical progress implicit in (4.1.1) and (4.1.2) are closely related to those used by Harrod (1949) and Hicks (1932) respectively. As an example of a relation that involves neutral technical progress in both senses we have the Cobb–Douglas relation

$$L = Be^{-\rho t}Y^{b}K^{1-b}, \tag{4.1.3}$$

where $b > 1$.

The model is completed by the equations

$$C = (1 - s)Y, \tag{4.1.4}$$

$$L_s = L_0e^{lt}, \tag{4.1.5}$$

$$Y = C + DK, \tag{4.1.6}$$

$$L = L_s, \tag{4.1.7}$$

where C and L_s denote real consumption and the labour supply respectively, and L_0 is a positive constant. The system comprising equations (4.1.1) and (4.1.4) to (4.1.7) determines the paths of Y, C, K, L_s and L.

Equation (4.1.4), which is a special case of both (3.1.1) and (3.5.1), assumes that a constant proportion of income is saved. Equation (4.1.5) assumes that the supply of labour grows at a constant proportional rate, and equation (4.1.6) that output equals demand. The latter equation can be regarded as the limiting case of (3.1.3) as $\lambda \longrightarrow \infty$.

Equation (4.1.7) assumes that the demand for labour equals the supply or, in other words, that there is full employment. We can regard this equation as a condition on DK. Thus it is assumed that, at any point of time, DK is such that the value of L obtained by eliminating C and Y from (4.1.1), (4.1.4) and (4.1.6) equals L_s.

Eliminating C, L and L_s from equations (4.1.1) and (4.1.4) to (4.1.7) we obtain the system

$$F(Y, K) = L_0 e^{(\rho+l)t}, \tag{4.1.8}$$

$$DK = sY. \tag{4.1.9}$$

This system has a particular solution

$$Y = Y^* e^{(\rho+l)t}, \tag{4.1.10}$$

$$K = K^* e^{(\rho+l)t}, \tag{4.1.11}$$

where Y^* and K^* are constants. For, substituting from (4.1.10) and (4.1.11) into (4.1.8) and (4.1.9) and remembering that F is homogenous of the first degree, we obtain

$$F(Y^*, K^*) = L_0, \tag{4.1.12}$$

$$(\rho + l)K^* = sY^*, \tag{4.1.13}$$

which are satisfied by

$$Y^* = \frac{(\rho + l)L_0}{F(\rho + l, s)}, \tag{4.1.14}$$

$$K^* = \frac{sL_0}{F(\rho + l, s)}. \tag{4.1.15}$$

We refer to $Y^* e^{(\rho+l)t}$ and $K^* e^{(\rho+l)t}$ as the *equilibrium growth paths* of output and capital respectively and $\rho + l$ as the *equilibrium growth rate.*

We shall now show that, assuming any initial values of Y and K which are positive and satisfy (4.1.8), the proportional deviations of these variables from their equilibrium growth paths tend to zero as $t \longrightarrow \infty$. Let y and k denote the logarithms of $Y/\{Y^* e^{(\rho+l)t}\}$ and $K/\{K^* e^{(\rho+l)t}\}$ respectively. Then we are required to show that $y \longrightarrow 0$ and $k \longrightarrow 0$ as $t \longrightarrow \infty$.

From (4.1.8) and the definitions of y and k we obtain

$$F(e^y Y^*, e^k K^*) = L_0, \tag{4.1.16}$$

and hence

$$F(e^{y-k} Y^*, K^*) = L_0 e^{-k}. \tag{4.1.17}$$

Moreover,

$$Dk = D \log K - \rho - l \tag{4.1.18}$$
$$= \frac{sY}{K} - \rho - l$$
$$= (\rho + l)(e^{y-k} - 1).$$

From (4.1.17) and (4.1.18) we obtain

$$F\left\{Y^*\left(\frac{Dk}{\rho + l} + 1\right), K^*\right\} = L_0 e^{-k}. \tag{4.1.19}$$

It follows from (4.1.19), (4.1.12) and the assumed properties of F that Dk is a continuous decreasing function of k which is defined for all k, and equal to zero when $k = 0$. Hence, whatever the initial value of k, we have

$$\lim_{t \to \infty} k = 0. \tag{4.1.20}$$

And it follows from (4.1.12), (4.1.17) and (4.1.20) that

$$\lim_{t \to \infty} y = 0. \tag{4.1.21}$$

It is, perhaps, surprising that the equilibrium growth rate is independent of propensity to save. But it is clear from (4.1.14) and (4.1.15) that an increase in s does raise the equilibrium growth paths of output and capital. Hence it does increase the average growth rates of these variables over a finite time interval. It also raises the equilibrium capital–output ratio, $\frac{K^*}{Y^*}$.

We turn now to the particular model in which (4.1.1) is replaced by (4.1.3). Replacing $F(\rho + l, s)$ by $B(\rho + l)^b s^{1-b}$ in (4.1.14) and (4.1.15) we obtain

$$Y^* = \frac{L_0}{B}\left\{\frac{s}{\rho + l}\right\}^{b-1}, \tag{4.1.22}$$

$$K^* = \frac{L_0}{B}\left\{\frac{s}{\rho + l}\right\}^{b}. \tag{4.1.23}$$

And (4.1.19) becomes

$$L_0 e^{-k} = BY^{*b}\left\{\frac{Dk}{\rho + l} + 1\right\}^b K^{*1-b}, \tag{4.1.24}$$
$$= L_0 \left\{\frac{Dk}{\rho + l} + 1\right\}^b.$$

From (4.1.24) we obtain

$$Dk = (\rho + l)(e^{-k/b} - 1), \tag{4.1.25}$$

whose solution is

(4.1.26) $$k = b \log \{(e^{k(0)/b} - 1)e^{-(\rho+l)t/b} + 1\}.$$

Then from (4.1.26) and the definition of k we obtain

(4.1.27) $$K = \{K(0)^{1/b} - K^{*1/b} + K^{*1/b}e^{(\rho+l)t/b}\}^b.$$

The path of Y can be derived from that of K by using

(4.1.28) $$Y = \{B^{-1}L_0e^{(\rho+l)t}K^{b-1}\}^{1/b},$$

which is obtained from (4.1.3), (4.1.5) and (4.1.7).

As an example of an application of the above model let us obtain predictions of Y and K under alternative assumptions about the propensity to save. Suppose that $B = 1{\cdot}0$, $L_0 = 100$, $b = 1{\cdot}5$, $\rho = 0{\cdot}04$, $l = 0{\cdot}01$, $Y(0) = 141$ and $K(0) = 282$. Then, if $s = 0{\cdot}1$, Y and K are on their equilibrium growth paths when $t = 0$ and will grow at a constant proportional rate. Their values after five, ten and twenty years are shown in the second and fourth columns of the following table:

t	Y		K		$\frac{K}{Y}$	
(in years)	$s = 0{\cdot}1$	$s = 0{\cdot}2$	$s = 0{\cdot}1$	$s = 0{\cdot}2$	$s = 0{\cdot}1$	$s = 0{\cdot}2$
0	141	141	282	282	2·00	2·00
5	180	195	360	449	2·00	2·30
10	233	264	465	679	2·00	2·57
20	384	468	767	1392	2·00	2·97

But, if, when $t = 0$, s increases (say because of some change in government fiscal policy) from 0·1 to 0·2, then the paths of Y and K will be as shown in the third and fifth columns of the table. The effect of the increase in s on $\frac{K}{Y}$ can be seen in the last two columns. Since $\frac{K^*}{Y^*} = \frac{s}{\rho + l}$, $\frac{K}{Y} \longrightarrow 4{\cdot}0$ as $t \longrightarrow \infty$.

The paths of $\frac{DK}{K}$ and $\frac{DY}{Y}$ can easily be obtained by using

(4.1.29) $$\frac{DK}{K} = \frac{sY}{K},$$

(4.1.30) $$\frac{DY}{Y} = \frac{\rho + l}{b} + \frac{(b-1)DK}{bK},$$

which follow from (4.1.9) and (4.1.28). After five years $\frac{DK}{K} = 0{\cdot}087$ and $\frac{DY}{Y} = 0{\cdot}062$, while after twenty years, $\frac{DK}{K} = 0{\cdot}067$ and $\frac{DY}{Y} = 0{\cdot}055$. Both $\frac{DK}{K}$ and $\frac{DY}{Y}$ will tend to 0·050 as $t \longrightarrow \infty$.

4.2 A Two-sector Model

Neither the model discussed in section 4.1 nor any of the models discussed in Chapter 3 allow for the effects of changes in the relative prices of consumers' goods and capital goods. They are formally equivalent to models of an economy that produces a single good which can either be consumed or transformed, at no cost, into fixed capital. This does not mean that they cannot be applied to an actual economy. But, in such applications, a single index of prices (e.g. an index of the prices of the components of the gross national product) will be used as a deflator for obtaining all real variables.

Our ultimate aim should, perhaps, be to construct multi-sector models which include different production functions for the different sectors and allow for the effects of changes in the relative prices of the goods produced by the different sectors. An important step towards this goal is the construction of two-sector models which include different production functions for consumers' goods and capital goods and allow for the effects of changes in the relative prices of these two types of good.

We turn now to the *two-sector neo-classical model* which is due to Meade (1960). We shall confine our attention to the case in which the production functions for both consumers' goods and capital goods are of the Cobb–Douglas type. The model is, then, as follows:

(4.2.1) $$L_c = B_1 e^{-\rho_1 t} C^{b_1} K_c^{1-b_1},$$

(4.2.2) $$L_\kappa = B_2 e^{-\rho_2 t} (DK)^{b_2} K_\kappa^{1-b_2},$$

(4.2.3) $$C = (1 - s) Y,$$

(4.2.4) $$p_c = (1 + \pi_1) w \frac{\partial L_c}{\partial C} = \frac{b_1(1 + \pi_1) w L_c}{C},$$

(4.2.5) $$p_\kappa = (1 + \pi_2) w \frac{\partial L_\kappa}{\partial (DK)} = \frac{b_2(1 + \pi_2) w L_\kappa}{DK},$$

(4.2.6) $$\frac{p_c C - w L_c}{p_\kappa K_c} = \frac{p_\kappa DK - w L_\kappa}{p_\kappa K_\kappa},$$

(4.2.7) $$L_s = L_0 e^{lt},$$

(4.2.8) $$L_c + L_\kappa = L_s,$$

(4.2.9) $$K_c + K_\kappa = K,$$

(4.2.10) $$Y = C + \frac{p_\kappa DK}{p_c},$$

where C, Y, K and L_s are as defined in the preceding section and

L_c = amount of labour used in the production of consumers' goods,
L_κ = amount of labour used in the production of capital goods,
K_c = amount of capital used in the production of consumers' goods,
K_κ = amount of capital used in the production of capital goods,
w = wage rate,
p_c = price of consumers' goods,
p_κ = price of capital goods,
$L_0, B_1, B_2, b_1, b_2, \rho_1, \rho_2, \pi_1, \pi_2, l, s$ = positive constants ($b_1, b_2 > 1$, $s < 1$).

The wage rate, w, is assumed to be exogenous.

Equations (4.2.1) and (4.2.2) assume that the amount of labour used in the production of consumer's goods is a function of real consumption, the amount of capital used in the production of consumers' goods, and time, while the amount of labour used in the production of capital goods is a function of the rate of investment, the amount of capital used in the production of capital goods, and time. Each of the functions is of the Cobb–Douglas type with neutral technical progress. But the parameters of the two functions, including the rates of technical progress, are, generally, assumed to be different.

Equation (4.2.3) is identical with (4.1.4). But care must now be taken over the definition of Y. We define Y as money income divided by p_c. Then the equation implies, like (4.1.4), that a constant proportion, s, of money income is saved.

Equation (4.2.4) assumes that the price of consumers' goods equals the short-run marginal cost of producing these goods plus a constant proportional margin π_1, which depends on the degree of imperfection of competition in the consumers' goods industries. Equation (4.2.5) is similar.

Equation (4.2.6) assumes that the rate of profit on capital used in the production of consumers' goods equals the rate of profit on capital used in the production of capital goods. We assume that this condition is preserved by the tendency for new capital to flow into the industry in which the rate of profit is greater.

Equation (4.2.7) is identical with (4.1.5), (4.2.8) assumes that there is full employment, (4.2.9) is an identity and (4.2.10) follows from the definition of real income.

Eliminating wL_c and wL_κ from (4.2.4), (4.2.5) and (4.2.6) we obtain

$$\text{(4.2.11)} \qquad \frac{p_c C}{p_\kappa DK} = \frac{b_1(1+\pi_1)\{b_2(1+\pi_2)-1\}K_c}{b_2(1+\pi_2)\{b_1(1+\pi_1)-1\}K_\kappa},$$

while, from (4.2.4) and (4.2.5), we obtain

$$\text{(4.2.12)} \qquad \frac{p_c C}{p_\kappa DK} = \frac{b_1(1+\pi_1)L_c}{b_2(1+\pi_2)L_\kappa},$$

and, from (4.2.3) and (4.2.10) we obtain

$$\frac{p_c C}{p_\kappa DK} = \frac{1}{s} - 1. \tag{4.2.13}$$

By substituting from (4.2.13) into (4.2.11) and (4.2.12) and using (4.2.7), (4.2.8) and (4.2.9) we obtain

$$L_\kappa = fL_0 e^{lt}, \tag{4.2.14}$$

$$K_\kappa = gK, \tag{4.2.15}$$

where
$$f = \frac{b_1(1+\pi_1)}{b_1(1+\pi_1) + b_2(1+\pi_2)\left(\frac{1}{s} - 1\right)},$$

$$g = \frac{b_1(1+\pi_1)\{b_2(1+\pi_2) - 1\}}{b_1(1+\pi_1)\{b_2(1+\pi_2) - 1\} + b_2(1+\pi_2)\left(\frac{1}{s} - 1\right)\{b_1(1+\pi_1) - 1\}}.$$

Then, from (4.2.2), (4.2.14) and (4.2.15), we obtain

$$fL_0 e^{lt} = B_2 e^{-\rho_2 t}(DK)^{b_2}(gK)^{1-b_2}, \tag{4.2.16}$$

which has a particular solution

$$K = K^* e^{(\rho_2 + l)t}, \tag{4.2.17}$$

where
$$K^* = \frac{fg^{b_2 - 1} L_0}{B_2(\rho_2 + l)^{b_2}}.$$

Equation (4.2.17) gives the equilibrium growth path of the total amount of capital in the economy. We note that the equilibrium growth rate of this variable is independent of both the propensity to save and the rate of technical progress in the production of consumers' goods. It depends only on the rate of growth of the labour supply and the rate of technical progress in the production of capital goods. But, since $\frac{\partial f}{\partial s} > 0$ and $\frac{\partial g}{\partial s} > 0$, we have $\frac{\partial K^*}{\partial s} > 0$. Hence, as in the simple neo-classical model, an increase in the propensity to save raises the equilibrium growth path of K. An interesting special case is that in which $b_1 = b_2$ and $\pi_1 = \pi_2$. In this case, we have $f = g = s$, and hence

$$K^* = \frac{L_0}{B_2}\left\{\frac{s}{\rho_2 + l}\right\}^{b_2},$$

which is similar to (4.1.23).

Now let k denote $\log \{K/K^* e^{(\rho_2 + l)t}\}$. Then, from (4.2.16), we obtain

$$\begin{aligned} \log f + (b_2 - 1)\log g - \log B_2 + \log L_0 + (\rho_2 + l)t \\ = b_2 \log(D \log K) + \log K \\ = b_2 \log(Dk + \rho_2 + l) + k + \log K^* + (\rho_2 + l)t, \end{aligned} \tag{4.2.18}$$

and hence

$$Dk = (\rho_2 + l)(e^{-k/b_2} - 1), \tag{4.2.19}$$

whose solution is

$$k = b_2 \log \{(e^{k(0)/b_2} - 1)e^{-(\rho_2+l)t/b_2} + 1\}. \tag{4.2.20}$$

Equation (4.2.20) implies that $\lim_{t\to\infty} k = 0$, so that the proportional deviation of K from its equilibrium growth path tends to zero as $t \longrightarrow \infty$. The path of K is given by

$$K = \{K(0)^{1/b_2} - K^{*1/b_2} + K^{*1/b_2}e^{(\rho_2+l)t/b_2}\}^{b_2}, \tag{4.2.21}$$

which follows from (4.2.20).

By substituting $L_c = (1-f)L_0e^{lt}$ and $K_c = (1-g)K$ into (4.2.1) we obtain

$$C = \left[\frac{(1-f)(1-g)^{b_1-1}K^{b_1-1}L_0e^{(\rho_1+l)t}}{B_1}\right]^{1/b_1} \tag{4.2.22}$$

which enables us to derive the path of C from that of K. Suppose, for example, that $K(0) = K^*$, so that K is on its equilibrium growth path. Then we have

$$C = \left[\frac{(1-f)(1-g)^{b_1-1}K^{*b_1-1}L_0e^{\{\rho_1+(b_1-1)\rho_2+b_1 l\}t}}{B_1}\right]^{1/b_1} \tag{4.2.23}$$

Hence the equilibrium growth rate of C equals $\rho_2 + l + \frac{\rho_1 - \rho_2}{b_1}$, which is greater or less than the equilibrium growth rate of K according as ρ_1 is greater or less than ρ_2. The path of Y can be obtained from that of C by using (4.2.3), while the path of p_c/p_κ can be obtained from those of C and K by using (4.2.13). It follows from the relation between the equilibrium growth rates of C and K that p_c/p_κ tends to zero or infinity according as ρ_1 is greater or less than ρ_2.

None of the results obtained so far depends on the behaviour of w. But it would be necessary to make some assumption about the behaviour of this variable in order to obtain the paths of p_c and p_κ. After obtaining the paths of the real variables in the system we can obtain the paths of p_c and p_κ associated with any assumed path of w from (4.2.4) and (4.2.5).

CHAPTER 5

MODELS OF CYCLICAL GROWTH

OUR next aim is to construct a model synthesising the essential features of the models discussed in Chapters 3 and 4. Whereas the models discussed in Chapter 3 assume that the path of output is unrelated to the productive capacity of the economy, those discussed in Chapter 4 assume that the economy is always producing to its full capacity. The empirical evidence suggests that the truth lies somewhere between these assumptions. There is a feed-back mechanism, involving variations in wages, prices and interest rates which is capable of ensuring that, over a long period, the actual path of output approximately follows that which would be associated with full employment, but not of preserving a continuous state of full employment. In Chapter 4 this mechanism was assumed to operate with infinite speed, while, in Chapter 3, it was ignored by treating the wage and interest rates as exogenous. In this chapter it will be formally introduced into the models, and will play an essential role in the synthesis of growth and cycles. The resulting model should be a more powerful tool, for either long- or short-term prediction, than those discussed in Chapters 3 and 4.

The first formal model in which a feed-back mechanism involving monetary phenomena plays an essential role in the synthesis of growth and cycles is due to Phillips (1961). But the mechanism was suggested by Keynes (1936). The following models differ from that of Phillips in that they incorporate a production function which allows for substitution between labour and capital. In this sense they are developments of the neo-classical model. They provide a synthesis of Keynesian and neo-classical theory.

5.1 A Basic Model

In this section we shall construct a basic model which will be extended and made more realistic in the following section. The equations of the basic model are:

(5.1.1) $$C = (1 - s)Y,$$

(5.1.2) $$\frac{DK}{K} = \gamma \log \left\{\frac{pY - wL}{(1 + c)rpK}\right\},$$

(5.1.3) $$DY = \lambda(C + DK - Y),$$

(5.1.4) $$L = Be^{-\rho t} Y^b K^{1-b},$$

(5.1.5) $$p = (1 + \pi)w\frac{\partial L}{\partial Y} = \frac{b(1 + \pi)wL}{Y},$$

(5.1.6) $$\frac{Dw}{w} = \beta \log\left\{\frac{L}{L_s}\right\} + a,$$

(5.1.7) $$\frac{M_d}{p} = AY^u r^{-v},$$

(5.1.8) $$M_d = M_s,$$

(5.1.9) $$L_s = L_0 e^{lt},$$

(5.1.10) $$M_s = M_0 e^{mt},$$

where
C = real consumption,
Y = real net income or output,
K = amount of fixed capital,
L = amount of labour employed,
L_s = supply of labour,
p = price level,
w = wage rate,
r = interest rate,
M_d = demand for money,
M_s = supply of money,
$a, b, c, l, m, s, u, v, \beta, \gamma, \lambda, \pi, \rho, A, B, L_0, M_0$ = positive constants ($b > 1, s < 1$).

Equations (5.1.1), (5.1.2), (5.1.3), (5.1.4) and (5.1.5) are identical with (4.1.4), (3.5.2), (3.1.3), (4.1.3) and (3.5.4) respectively, and have been discussed in the preceding chapters.

Equation (5.1.6) is a price-adjustment equation applied to the labour market. It assumes that the proportional rate of increase in the wage rate is an increasing function of the proportion of the labour force employed. Underlying this assumption is the hypothesis that, if the proportion of the labour force employed exceeds a certain level, competition for labour will cause the wage rate to increase, while, if the proportion of the labour force employed is less than this level, competition for jobs will cause the wage rate to decrease. A study by Phillips (1958) of United Kingdom data for the period 1862–1957 indicates that, during this period, wages tended to rise or fall according as the proportion of the labour force employed was greater or less than about 0·95.

The variable M_d in equation (5.1.7) is the amount of their assets which firms and individuals wish to hold in the form of money (i.e. cash and bank deposits). The equation assumes that the real demand for money, $\frac{M_d}{p}$ is greater, the greater is real income and the lower is the interest rate. Keynes (1936), who was the first to explore the consequences of the dependence of the demand for money on the interest rate, suggested two reasons for this dependence. The first is that interest is the cost of holding money rather than securities. The second is that the likelihood of an increase in the interest rate is greater, the lower is the existing rate, and, if the expected increase in the interest rate is sufficiently great, it will be profitable to postpone the purchase of securities (i.e. hold money) until after the increase has occurred. The reasons for assuming the demand for money to depend on income are more obvious. We note, in particular, that the demand for money is related to the amount of payments expected to be made in the near future, and that this amount is related to income.

Equation (5.1.8) implicitly assumes that the interest rate varies in such a way that the demand for money always equals the supply. The justification for this assumption is that, if the demand for money exceeds the supply, the pressure to sell securities will cause a fall in their price which is equivalent to a rise in the interest rate. And, because of (5.1.7), a rise in the interest rate will tend to eliminate the excess demand for money. Similarly, an excess supply of money will cause the interest rate to fall; and this will tend to eliminate the excess supply of money. Equation (5.1.8) assumes that these processes are instantaneous. A more realistic assumption, which can easily be incorporated in the model is that

$$\frac{Dr}{r} = h \log \left\{\frac{M_d}{M_s}\right\}, \tag{5.1.11}$$

where h is a positive constant. But, if h is large relative to γ, λ and β, the error resulting from the use of (5.1.8) instead of (5.1.11) is small. We assume, for simplicity, that this is so.

Equation (5.1.9) assumes that the labour supply increases at a constant proportional rate and equation (5.1.10) that the money supply increases at a constant proportional rate. The interpretation of the latter assumption is that monetary policy is neutral. The way in which the behaviour of the system is modified when the money supply is changed in response to changes in the other variables in the model will be discussed in Chapter 6.

Eliminating wL from (5.1.2) and (5.1.5) we obtain

$$D \log K = \gamma (\log Y - \log K - \log r) + \gamma \log \left\{\frac{b(1+\pi)-1}{b(1+\pi)(1+c)}\right\}. \tag{5.1.12}$$

And, from (5.1.7), (5.1.8) and (5.1.10) we obtain

$$\log r = \frac{u}{v} \log Y + \frac{1}{v} \log p - \frac{mt}{v} + \frac{1}{v} \log \left\{\frac{A}{M_0}\right\}. \tag{5.1.13}$$

From (5.1.12) and (5.1.13) we obtain

$$D \log K = \gamma\left(1 - \frac{u}{v}\right) \log Y - \gamma \log K - \frac{\gamma}{v} \log p + \frac{\gamma mt}{v} + \gamma\left[\log \left\{\frac{b(1+\pi)-1}{b(1+\pi)(1+c)}\right\} - \frac{1}{v} \log \left\{\frac{A}{M_0}\right\}\right], \tag{5.1.14}$$

which, together with (5.1.4) and (5.1.5), yields

$$(5.1.15)\quad D \log K = \frac{\gamma}{v}(1 + v - u - b) \log Y - \frac{\gamma}{v}(1 + v - b) \log K$$

$$- \frac{\gamma}{v} \log w + \frac{\gamma}{v}(m + \rho)t$$

$$+ \frac{\gamma}{v}\left[v \log \left\{\frac{b(1 + \pi) - 1}{b(1 + \pi)(1 + c)}\right\} + \log \left\{\frac{M_0}{b(1 + \pi)AB}\right\}\right].$$

From (5.1.4), (5.1.6) and (5.1.9) we obtain

$$(5.1.16)\quad D \log w = \beta b \log Y - \beta(b - 1) \log K - \beta(\rho + l)t + a + \beta \log \left\{\frac{B}{L_0}\right\},$$

and, from (5.1.1) and (5.1.3)

$$(5.1.17)\quad D \log Y = \lambda \left\{\frac{K}{Y} D \log K - s\right\}.$$

The paths of w, K and Y are determined by their initial values and the system comprising equations (5.1.15) to (5.1.17). This system has a particular solution

$$(5.1.18)\quad w = w^* e^{\{(1-u)(\rho+l)+m-l\}t},$$

$$(5.1.19)\quad K = K^* e^{(\rho+l)t},$$

$$(5.1.20)\quad Y = Y^* e^{(\rho+l)t},$$

where w^*, K^* and Y^* are constants. For, substituting from equations (5.1.18) to (5.1.20) into equations (5.1.15) to (5.1.17) we obtain

$$(5.1.21)\quad \rho + l = \frac{\gamma}{v}(1 + v - u - b) \log Y^* - \frac{\gamma}{v}(1 + v - b) \log K^*$$

$$- \frac{\gamma}{v} \log w^* + \frac{\gamma}{v}\left[v \log \left\{\frac{b(1 + \pi) - 1}{b(1 + \pi)(1 + c)}\right\} + \log \left\{\frac{M_0}{b(1 + \pi)AB}\right\}\right],$$

$$(5.1.22)\quad (1 - u)(\rho + l) + m - l = \beta b \log Y^* - \beta(b - 1) \log K^* + a + \beta(\log B - \log L_0),$$

$$(5.1.23)\quad \rho + l = \lambda\left\{\frac{K^*}{Y^*}(\rho + l) - s\right\},$$

which are satisfied by

$$(5.1.24)\quad \log w^* = \log\left\{\frac{M_0}{b(1+\pi)AB}\right\} - u\log\left\{\frac{L_0}{B}\right\} + v\log\left\{\frac{b(1+\pi)-1}{b(1+\pi)(1+c)}\right\} - \{v-(1-u)(b-1)\}$$

$$\log\left\{\frac{\rho+l+\lambda s}{\lambda(\rho+l)}\right\} + \frac{u}{\beta}\{a+l-m-(1-u)(\rho+l)\} - \frac{v}{\gamma}(\rho+l),$$

$$(5.1.25)\quad \log K^* = \log\left\{\frac{L_0}{B}\right\} + b\log\left\{\frac{\rho+l+\lambda s}{\lambda(\rho+l)}\right\} - \frac{1}{\beta}\{a+l-m-(1-u)(\rho+l)\},$$

$$(5.1.26)\quad \log Y^* = \log\left\{\frac{L_0}{B}\right\} + (b-1)\log\left\{\frac{\rho+l+\lambda s}{\lambda(\rho+l)}\right\} - \frac{1}{\beta}\{a+l-m-(1-u)(\rho+l)\}.$$

Hence, as in the case of the simple neo-classical model, the equilibrium growth rate of K and Y equals $\rho + l$, and the levels of the equilibrium growth paths of these variables are higher, the greater is the propensity to save. But an interesting new property of the model under discussion is that the levels of the equilibrium growth paths of K and Y are higher the greater is m, the proportional rate of increase in the supply of money. The reason for this is that, when K and Y are on their equilibrium growth paths, the proportion of the labour force employed is an increasing function of m. For, substituting from (5.1.18) into (5.1.6) we obtain

$$(5.1.27)\qquad \log\left\{\frac{L}{L_s}\right\} = -\frac{1}{\beta}\{a+l-m-(1-u)(\rho+l)\},$$

and it follows from (5.1.9) that the equilibrium growth path of employment is given by

$$(5.1.28)\qquad L = L^* e^{lt},$$

where $\log L^* = \log L_0 - \frac{1}{\beta}\{a+l-m-(1-u)(\rho+l)\}.$

We implicitly assume that $m < l + a - (1-u)(\rho+l)$. Otherwise the model breaks down. For the amount of labour employed cannot exceed the labour supply.

It follows from (5.1.18) that the equilibrium rate of increase in the wage rate equals $(1-u)(\rho+l)+m-l$, and, from (5.1.5), (5.1.18), (5.1.20) and (5.1.28) that the equilibrium rate of increase in the price level equals $m - u(\rho+l)$. Hence, if $u = 1$, the equilibrium rate of increase in the price level equals the rate of increase in the money supply minus the sum of the rate of increase in the labour supply and the rate of increase in the productivity of labour resulting from technical progress. The parameter u is the *income elasticity of demand for money*. The condition that $u = 1$ implies that, when the interest rate is constant, a given proportional increase in income causes an equal proportional increase in the demand for money.

It follows from (5.1.12), (5.1.25) and (5.1.26) that, when Y and K are on their equilibrium growth paths, the interest rate equals the constant r^* given by

$$\text{(5.1.29)} \quad \log r^* = \log\left[\frac{\lambda(\rho + l)\{b(1+\pi) - 1\}}{b(\rho + l + \lambda s)(1 + \pi)(1 + c)}\right] - \frac{\rho + l}{\gamma}.$$

We note that $\dfrac{\partial r^*}{\partial b} > 0$ and $\dfrac{\partial r^*}{\partial s} < 0$. The interpretation of these results is that the equilibrium interest rate is higher, the more important is capital in the productive process and the lower is the propensity to save. Another interesting property of (5.1.29) is that r^* is independent of the supply of money and the *liquidity preference* parameters, A, u and v. The explanation of this result is that, when all variables are on their equilibrium growth paths, the wage rate is so adjusted to the money supply and the liquidity preference parameters as to neutralise their influence on the interest rate and the real variables in the system.

Equations (5.1.13) and (5.1.29) clarify the relation between the Keynesian and classical theories of interest. According to the classical theory the interest rate is determined by the real phenomena affecting saving and the demand for capital, whereas, according to the Keynesian theory monetary phenomena play a predominant role in determining the interest rate. In the model under discussion the Keynesian theory, which can be represented by (5.1.13), applies to the actual interest rate at any point of time, while the classical theory, which can be represented by (5.1.29), applies to the equilibrium interest rate only.

From equations (5.1.15) to (5.1.17) and (5.1.24) to (5.1.26) we obtain

$$\text{(5.1.30)} \quad Dy_1 = -\beta(b - 1)y_2 + \beta b y_3,$$

$$\text{(5.1.31)} \quad Dy_2 = -\frac{\gamma}{v}y_1 - \frac{\gamma}{v}(1 + v - b)y_2 + \frac{\gamma}{v}(1 + v - u - b)y_3,$$

$$\text{(5.1.32)} \quad Dy_3 = \left\{\frac{\rho + l + \lambda_s}{\rho + l}\right\}e^{y_2 - y_3}Dy_2 + (\rho + l + \lambda s)(e^{y_2 - y_3} - 1).$$

where
$$y_1 = \log\{w/w^* e^{\{(1-u)(\rho+l)+m-l\}t}\},$$
$$y_2 = \log\{K/K^* e^{(\rho+l)t}\},$$
$$y_3 = \log\{Y/Y^* e^{(\rho+l)t}\}.$$

Then, from (5.1.31) and (5.1.32), we obtain

$$(5.1.33)\quad Dy_3 = \left\{\frac{\rho + l + \lambda s}{\rho + l}\right\}\left\{-\frac{\gamma}{v}y_1 - \frac{\gamma}{v}(1 + v - b)y_2 + \frac{\gamma}{v}(1 + v - u - b)y_3\right\}e^{y_2 - y_3} + (\rho + l + \lambda s)(e^{y_2 - y_3} - 1) =$$

$$-\frac{\gamma(\rho + l + \lambda s)}{v(\rho + l)}y_1 + (\rho + l + \lambda s)\left\{1 - \frac{\gamma(1 + v - b)}{v(\rho + l)}\right\}y_2 + (\rho + l + \lambda s)\left\{\frac{\gamma(1 + v - u - b)}{v(\rho + l)} - 1\right\}y_3 + \phi(y_1, y_2, y_3),$$

where $\dfrac{\phi(y_1, y_2, y_3)}{|y_1| + |y_2| + |y_3|}$ tends to zero as y_1, y_2 and y_3 tend to zero.

The exact paths of the y_i's are determined by their initial values and equations (5.1.30), (5.1.31) and (5.1.33) and the approximate paths by the initial values and the linear system

$$(5.1.34)\qquad Dy = Fy,$$

obtained by omitting $\phi(y_1, y_2, y_3)$. A sufficient condition for the proportional deviations of w, K and Y from their equilibrium growth paths to tend to zero as $t \to \infty$ is that the corresponding initial proportional deviations are not too large and the characteristic roots of F have negative real parts.

The characteristic roots of F are the roots of

$$(5.1.35)\qquad x^3 + a_1x^2 + a_2x + a_3 = 0,$$

where

$$a_1 = \rho + l + \lambda s + \frac{\gamma u}{v} + \frac{\gamma\lambda s(b + u - v - 1)}{v(\rho + l)},$$

$$a_2 = \frac{\gamma u}{v}(\rho + l + \lambda s) + \frac{\gamma\beta}{v}\left(1 + \frac{\lambda sb}{\rho + l}\right),$$

$$a_3 = \frac{\gamma\beta}{v}(\rho + l + \lambda s).$$

Necessary and sufficient conditions for these roots to have negative real parts are: $a_1 > 0$, $a_3 > 0$, $a_1a_2 - a_3 > 0$. These conditions will be satisfied provided that $b + u - v > 1$, but may not be satisfied otherwise. Hence a strong influence of income on the demand for money (i.e. a high value of u) has a stabilising effect, while a strong influence of the interest rate on the demand for money (i.e. a high value of v) has a destabilising effect.

Some illumination of this property of the model may be provided by a non-mathematical description of the effects of a disturbance of the *steady state*. Suppose that all variables are on their equilibrium growth paths and that some disturbance causes an increase in the proportional rate of growth of real consumption. This will cause an increase in the proportional rate of increase in output, employment and the price level. The increases in the proportional rates of increase in real income and the price level will each tend to increase the proportional rate of increase in the demand for money. Hence, provided that there is no change in the proportional rate of increase in the supply of money, there will be a rise in the interest rate. The rise in the interest rate will tend to decrease the proportional rate of increase in the demand for capital goods, and hence check the upward deviation of output from its equilibrium growth path. Thus a strong influence of income on the demand for money can be expected to have a stabilising effect. But the rise in the interest rate caused by the increases in the proportional rates of increase in real income and prices will be smaller, the more important is the influence of the interest rate on the demand for money. For, because of (5.1.8), the decrease in the demand for money caused by the rise in the interest rate must be just sufficient to offset the increase in the demand for money caused by the upward deviations of real income and the price level from their equilibrium growth paths. Thus a strong influence of the interest rate on the demand for money can be expected to have a destabilising effect.

Keynes (1936) suggested that the *interest elasticity of demand for money*, $\frac{\partial M_d}{\partial r} \Big/ \frac{M_d}{r}$, may be an increasing function of r and tend to minus infinity as r tends, from above, to some positive number. Equation (5.1.7) implies that the interest elasticity of demand for money is a constant, $-v$. If Keynes' hypothesis were correct, this would be a serious defect of our model. But, so far, there has been little empirical support for the hypothesis. Indeed, an analysis by Bronfenbrenner and Mayer (1960) of United States data for the period 1919–56 failed to reject the hypothesis that the interest elasticity of demand for money is constant.

Let us assume, for an example, that $\rho = 0{\cdot}04$, $l = 0{\cdot}01$, $s = 0{\cdot}20$, $b = 1{\cdot}50$, $\lambda = 4{\cdot}00$, $\gamma = 0{\cdot}20$ and $\beta = 2{\cdot}00$.

The parameter β is approximately equal to the increase in the percentage rate of increase in the wage rate associated with a 1 per cent increase in the level of employment. The assumed value of this parameter is suggested by data for the United Kingdom (see Phillips (1958)). The other parameters have been interpreted in Chapters 3 and 4. For the above values of the parameters other than u and v the stability condition is

$$v < 1{\cdot}45u - 0{\cdot}75 + \frac{34}{0{\cdot}40u + 24}. \tag{5.1.36}$$

If, as is often assumed, $u = 1$, this condition is satisfied for $v < 2{\cdot}10$, while, even if $u = 0$, the condition is satisfied for $v < 0{\cdot}67$. The various empirical estimates of the interest elasticity of demand for money in the United Kingdom and United States lie within the range 0 to $-2{\cdot}0$ (see

Bronfenbrenner and Mayer (1960) and Teigen (1964)). For realistic values of u and v satisfying (5.1.36) two of the roots of (5.1.35) are complex so that the model generates a damped cycle about a trend towards the equilibrium growth path.

5.2 Some Extensions

We have shown that, for plausible values of the parameters, the model constructed in section 5.1 generates damped oscillations of output about a long-term upward trend. In this respect the model is more realistic than those discussed in Chapters 3 and 4. But it has one implication that is unrealistic and, indeed, physically impossible. This is that the level of stocks must tend to minus infinity as $t \longrightarrow \infty$. For the rate of increase in stocks equals $Y - C - DK$ which, in view of (5.1.3), must be negative when Y is on its equilibrium growth path. This implication of the model is a consequence of neglecting the influence of stocks on production.

We now take account of this influence by replacing (5.1.3) by

$$DY = \lambda(C + DK - Y) + \mu(S^0 - S), \tag{5.2.1}$$

where S^0 and S denote the desired and actual stock levels respectively, and μ is a positive constant. This equation is identical with (3.3.1) and has the same interpretation. At the same time we introduce a time-lag into the consumption relation by replacing (5.1.1) by

$$\frac{DC}{C} = \alpha \log \left\{\frac{(1-s)Y}{C}\right\}, \tag{5.2.2}$$

where α is a positive constant. This equation is a special case of (3.5.21).

To complete the model we add

$$S^0 = f(C + DK), \tag{5.2.3}$$

$$DS = Y - C - DK, \tag{5.2.4}$$

where f is a positive constant. Equation (5.2.3) is a special case of (3.3.2), while (5.2.4) is identical with (3.3.3). The revised model then comprises the twelve equations (5.1.2), (5.1.4) to (5.1.10) and (5.2.1) to (5.2.4) and determines the paths of the twelve variables C, Y, K, L, L_s, p, w, r, M_d, M_s, S^0 and S.

As before, from (5.1.4), (5.1.6) and (5.1.9) we obtain

$$D \log w = \beta b \log Y - \beta(b-1) \log K - \beta(\rho + l)t + a + \beta \log \left\{\frac{B}{L_0}\right\}, \tag{5.2.5}$$

which is identical with (5.1.16), while, from (5.1.2), (5.1.4), (5.1.5), (5.1.7), (5.1.8) and (5.1.10), we obtain

$$(5.2.6)\quad D\log K = \frac{\gamma}{v}(1+v-u-b)\log Y - \frac{\gamma}{v}(1+v-b)\log K$$
$$-\frac{\gamma}{v}\log w + \frac{\gamma}{v}(m+\rho)t$$
$$+\frac{\gamma}{v}\left[v\log\left\{\frac{b(1+\pi)-1}{b(1+\pi)(1+c)}\right\} + \log\left\{\frac{M_0}{b(1+\pi)AB}\right\}\right],$$

which is identical with (5.1.15). From (5.2.1) and (5.2.3) we obtain

$$(5.2.7)\quad D\log Y = (\lambda+\mu f)\frac{C}{Y} + (\lambda+\mu f)\frac{K}{Y}D\log K - \mu\frac{S}{Y} - \lambda,$$

from (5.2.2)

$$(5.2.8)\qquad D\log C = \alpha\,(\log Y - \log C) + \alpha\log(1-s),$$

and from (5.2.4)

$$(5.2.9)\qquad D\log S = \frac{Y}{S} - \frac{C}{S} - \frac{K}{S}D\log K.$$

The paths of w, K, Y, C and S are determined by their initial values and the system comprising equations (5.2.5) to (5.2.9). This system has a particular solution

$$(5.2.10)\qquad w = w^* e^{\{(1-u)(\rho+l)+m-l\}t},$$

$$(5.2.11)\qquad K = K^* e^{(\rho+l)t},$$

$$(5.2.12)\qquad Y = Y^* e^{(\rho+l)t},$$

$$(5.2.13)\qquad C = C^* e^{(\rho+l)t},$$

$$(5.2.14)\qquad S = S^* e^{(\rho+l)t},$$

where:

$$(5.2.15)\quad \log w^* = \log\left\{\frac{M_0}{b(1+\pi)AB}\right\} - u\log\left\{\frac{L_0}{B}\right\}$$
$$+ v\log\left\{\frac{b(1+\pi)-1}{b(1+\pi)(1+)c}\right\} - \{v-(1-u)(b-1)\}\log q$$
$$+\frac{u}{\beta}\{a+l-m-(1-u)(\rho+l)\} - \frac{v}{\gamma}(\rho+l),$$

$$(5.2.16)\quad \log K^* = \log\left\{\frac{L_0}{B}\right\} + b\log q - \frac{1}{\beta}\{a+l-m$$
$$-(1-u)(\rho+l)\},$$

$$\text{(5.2.17)}\quad \log Y^* = \log\left\{\frac{L_0}{B}\right\} + (b-1)\log q - \frac{1}{\beta}\{a + l - m - (1-u)(\rho + l)\},$$

$$\text{(5.2.18)}\quad \log C^* = \log\left\{\frac{(1-s)L_0}{B}\right\} + (b-1)\log q - \frac{1}{\beta}\{a + l - m - (1-u)(\rho + l)\} - \frac{\rho + l}{\alpha},$$

$$\text{(5.2.19)}\quad \log S^* = \log\left\{\frac{L_0}{B}\right\} + (b-1)\log q - \frac{1}{\beta}\{a + l - m - (1-u)(\rho + l)\} + \log\left\{\frac{\mu f - \rho - l}{\mu + (\rho + l)(\lambda + \mu f)}\right\},$$

$$\text{(5.2.20)}\quad q = \frac{K^*}{Y^*} = \frac{\mu + (\rho + l)(\rho + l + \lambda)}{(\rho + l)\{\mu + (\rho + l)(\lambda + \mu f)\}} - \frac{(1-s)e^{-(\rho+l)/\alpha}}{\rho + l}.$$

We assume that

$$\text{(5.2.21)}\quad \mu + (\rho + l)(\rho + l + \lambda) - \{\mu + (\rho + l)(\lambda + \mu f)\}(1-s)e^{-(\rho+l)/\alpha} > 0,$$

$$\text{(5.2.22)}\quad \mu f - \rho - l > 0.$$

The inequalities (5.2.21) and (5.2.22) are necessary and sufficient conditions for $S^* > 0$, while (5.2.21) is a necessary and sufficient condition for $w^* > 0$, $K^* > 0$, $Y^* > 0$ and $C^* > 0$. Both inequalities are satisfied for plausible values of the parameters. We note that, as $\alpha \longrightarrow \infty$ and $\mu \longrightarrow 0$, the expressions for w^*, K^* and Y^* given by (5.2.15) to (5.2.17) tend to those given by (5.1.24) to (5.1.26).

From equations (5.2.5) to (5.2.9) and (5.2.15) to (5.2.20) we obtain

$$\text{(5.2.23)}\quad Dy_1 = \beta(b-1)y_2 + \beta b y_3,$$

$$\text{(5.2.24)}\quad Dy_2 = -\frac{\gamma}{v}y_1 - \frac{\gamma}{v}(1 + v - b)y_2 + \frac{\gamma}{v}(1 + v - u - b)y_3,$$

$$\text{(5.2.25)}\quad Dy_3 = q(\lambda + \mu f)e^{y_2 - y_3}Dy_2 + q(\rho + l)(\lambda + \mu f)(e^{y_2 - y_3} - 1) + \{(\lambda + \mu f)(1-s)e^{-(\rho+l)/\alpha}\}(e^{y_4 - y_3} - 1) - \frac{\mu(\mu f - \rho - l)}{\mu + (\rho + l)(\lambda + \mu f)}(e^{y_5 - y_3} - 1),$$

$$\text{(5.2.26)}\quad Dy_4 = \alpha(y_3 - y_4),$$

$$\text{(5.2.27)}\quad Dy_5 = \frac{\mu + (\rho + l)(\lambda + \mu f)}{\mu f - \rho - l}\{-qe^{y_2 - y_5}Dy_2 - q(\rho + l)(e^{y_2 - y_5} - 1) + e^{y_3 - y_5} - 1 - (1-s)e^{-(\rho+l)/\alpha}(e^{y_4 - y_5} - 1)\},$$

where $y_1 = \log \{w/w^* e^{\{(1-u)(\rho+l)+m-l\}t}\}$,

$y_2 = \log \{K/K^* e^{(\rho+l)t}\}$,

$y_3 = \log \{Y/Y^* e^{(\rho+l)t}\}$,

$y_4 = \log \{C/C^* e^{(\rho+l)t}\}$,

$y_5 = \log \{S/S^* e^{(\rho+l)t}$.

Then, from (5.2.24), (5.2.25) and (5.2.27) we obtain

(5.2.28)
$$Dy_3 = -\frac{\gamma q}{v}(\lambda+\mu f)y_1 - q(\lambda+\mu f)\left\{\frac{\gamma}{v}(1+v-b)-\rho-l\right\}y_2 + \left[q(\lambda+\mu f)\left\{\frac{\gamma}{v}(1+v-u-b)-\rho-l\right\} - (\lambda+\mu f)(1-s)e^{-(\rho+l)/\alpha} + \left\{\frac{\mu(\mu f-\rho-l)}{\mu+(\rho+l)(\lambda+\mu f)}\right\}\right]y_3 + \{(\lambda+\mu f)(1-s)e^{-(\rho+l)/\alpha}\}y_4 - \left\{\frac{\mu(\mu f-\rho-l)}{\mu+(\rho+l)(\lambda+\mu f)}\right\}y_5 + \phi(y_1, y_2, y_3, y_4, y_5),$$

(5.2.29)
$$Dy_5 = \left\{\frac{\mu+(\rho+l)(\lambda+\mu f)}{\mu f-\rho-l}\right\}\left[\frac{\gamma q}{v}y_1 + \left\{\frac{\gamma q}{v}(1+v-b) - q(\rho+l)\right\}y_2 + \left\{1-\frac{\gamma q}{v}(1+v-u-b)\right\}y_3 - \{(1-s)e^{-(\rho+l)/\alpha}\}y_4 + \{q(\rho+l)-1+(1-s)e^{-(\rho+l)/\alpha}\}y_5\right] + \psi(y_1, y_2, y_3, y_4, y_5),$$

where $\phi(y_1, y_2, y_3, y_4, y_5)\Big/\sum_{i=1}^{5}|y_i|$ and $\psi(y_1, y_2, y_3, y_4, y_5)\Big/\sum_{i=1}^{5}|y_i|$, each tend to zero as the y_i's tend to zero.

The exact paths of the y_i's are determined by their initial values and equations (5.2.23), (5.2.24), (5.2.26), (5.2.28) and (5.2.29), and the approximate paths by the initial values and the linear system obtained by omitting $\phi(y_1, y_2, y_3, y_4, y_5)$ and $\psi(y_1, y_2, y_3, y_4, y_5)$. Suppose, for example, that $\rho = 0{\cdot}04$, $l = 0{\cdot}01$, $s = 0{\cdot}20$, $b = 1{\cdot}50$, $\lambda = 4{\cdot}00$, $\gamma = 0{\cdot}20$, $\beta = 2{\cdot}00$, $\alpha = 1{\cdot}00$, $u = 1{\cdot}00$, $v = 1{\cdot}00$, $\mu = 2{\cdot}00$, $f = 0{\cdot}50$. Then the approximate linear system is

(5.2.30)
$$Dy = Fy$$

where

$$y = \begin{bmatrix} y_1 \\ y_2 \\ y_3 \\ y_4 \\ y_5 \end{bmatrix}, \quad F = \begin{bmatrix} 0{\cdot}00 & -1{\cdot}00 & 3{\cdot}00 & 0{\cdot}00 & 0{\cdot}00 \\ -0{\cdot}20 & -0{\cdot}10 & -0{\cdot}10 & 0{\cdot}00 & 0{\cdot}00 \\ -4{\cdot}35 & -1{\cdot}09 & -6{\cdot}23 & 3{\cdot}81 & -0{\cdot}84 \\ 0{\cdot}00 & 0{\cdot}00 & 1{\cdot}00 & -1{\cdot}00 & 0{\cdot}00 \\ 2{\cdot}06 & 0{\cdot}52 & 3{\cdot}39 & -1{\cdot}80 & -0{\cdot}05 \end{bmatrix}.$$

The characteristic roots of F are: $-0{\cdot}034$, $-0{\cdot}45$, $-3{\cdot}25$, $-1{\cdot}82 + (0{\cdot}77)i$, $-1{\cdot}82 - (0{\cdot}77)i$. Thus the model generates a damped cycle about a trend towards the equilibrium growth path. Moreover, the period of the cycle is approximately 8 years. We conclude, therefore, that there are plausible values of the parameters for which the model generates paths of output, employment and prices very similar to those relating to actual economies.

The small negative root, $-0{\cdot}034$ is associated with the slow convergence of $\log K$ to its equilibrium growth path, after $\log L$ has approximately reached its equilibrium growth path. It is approximately equal to $\frac{\rho + l}{b}$, the approximate proportional rate of decrease of $|\log \{K/K^* e^{(\rho+l)t}\}|$ in the simple neo-classical model (see equation (4.1.26)).

CHAPTER 6

ECONOMIC REGULATION

OUR aim, in this chapter, is to show how the behaviour of a cyclical growth model is modified by the introduction of various feed-back relations representing monetary and fiscal policies. This can be regarded as a problem of prediction in the broadest sense and illustrates one of the main potential applications of economic models by governments. Moreover, to the extent that governments adopt the sort of policies to be considered, it is important, even for the purpose of pure forecasting, that the feed-back relations involved should be built into the model.

In order to keep the algebra as simple as possible we shall work with the basic model given in section 5.1. But the whole argument can be repeated for the more realistic model given in section 5.2, and the main conclusions are unaffected.

6.1 Monetary Policy

In Chapter 5 monetary policy was assumed to be neutral in the sense that the money supply increases at a constant proportional rate. We shall now assume that the money supply is changed continuously in response to changes in the other variables in the model.

We consider, first, the policy represented by

$$\log M_s = \log \hat{M} + \theta \log \left\{\frac{\hat{L}e^{lt}}{L}\right\}, \tag{6.1.1}$$

where $\hat{L}$, $\hat{M}$ and θ are positive constants. We assume that $\hat{L}e^{lt}$ is the path of employment that is considered to be optimal. Since the labour supply follows the path L_0e^{lt}, the optimum proportional level of employment is $\frac{\hat{L}}{L_0}$. This ratio, which must not exceed unity, reflects what is considered to be the optimum balance between unemployment and inflation. Equation (6.1.1) assumes that, when employment is at the optimum level, the money supply is held constant, at $\hat{M}$, and that otherwise, the proportional excess of M_s over $\hat{M}$ is an increasing function of the proportional excess of $\hat{L}e^{lt}$ over L. Equation (6.1.1) now replaces (5.1.10), so that the model comprises equations (5.1.1) to (5.1.9) and (6.1.1).

From (5.1.7), (5.1.8) and (6.1.1) we obtain

$$\log r = \frac{u}{v}\log Y + \frac{1}{v}\log p + \frac{\theta}{v}\log L - \frac{\theta lt}{v} + \frac{1}{v}\log\left\{\frac{A}{\hat{M}}\right\} - \frac{\theta}{v}\log \hat{L}. \tag{6.1.2}$$

Then, from (5.1.12) and (6.1.2), we obtain

$$(6.1.3)\quad D\log K=\gamma\left(1-\frac{u}{v}\right)\log Y-\gamma\log K-\frac{\gamma}{v}\log p-\frac{\gamma\theta}{v}\log L$$
$$+\frac{\gamma\theta lt}{v}+\gamma\left[\log\left\{\frac{b(1+\pi)-1}{b(1+\pi)(1+c)}\right\}-\frac{1}{v}\log\left\{\frac{A}{\hat{M}}\right\}+\frac{\theta}{v}\log\hat{L}\right],$$

which, together with (5.1.4) and (5.1.5), yields

$$(6.1.4)\quad D\log K=\frac{\gamma}{v}\{1+v-u-(1+\theta)b\}\log Y$$
$$-\frac{\gamma}{v}\{v-(1+\theta)(b-1)\}\log K-\frac{\gamma}{v}\log w+\frac{\gamma}{v}\{\rho+\theta(\rho+l)\}t$$
$$+\frac{\gamma}{v}\left[v\log\left\{\frac{b(1+\pi)-1}{b(1+\pi)(1+c)}\right\}+\log\left\{\frac{\hat{M}}{b(1+\pi)AB}\right\}\right.$$
$$\left.+\theta\log\left\{\frac{\hat{L}}{B}\right\}\right].$$

We also have

$$(6.1.5)\quad D\log w=\beta b\log Y-\beta(b-1)\log K-\beta(\rho+l)t+a$$
$$+\beta\log\left\{\frac{B}{L_0}\right\},$$

$$(6.1.6)\qquad D\log Y=\lambda\left\{\frac{K}{Y}D\log K-s\right\},$$

which are identical with (5.1.16) and (5.1.17) respectively.

The paths of w, K and Y are determined by their initial values and the system comprising equations (6.1.4) to (6.1.6). This system has a particular solution:

$$(6.1.7)\qquad w=w^{*}e^{\{(1-u)(\rho+l)-l\}t},$$

$$(6.1.8)\qquad K=K^{*}e^{(\rho+l)t},$$

$$(6.1.9)\qquad Y=Y^{*}e^{(\rho+l)t},$$

where

$$(6.1.10)\quad \log w^{*}=\log\left\{\frac{\hat{M}}{b(1+\pi)AB}\right\}-u\log\left\{\frac{L_0}{B}\right\}+\theta\log\left\{\frac{\hat{L}}{L_0}\right\}$$
$$+v\log\left\{\frac{b(1+\pi)-1}{b(1+\pi)(1+c)}\right\}-\{v-(1-u)(b-1)\}\log\left\{\frac{\rho+l+\lambda s}{\lambda(\rho+l)}\right\}$$
$$+\frac{u+\theta}{\beta}\{a+l-(1-u)(\rho+l)\}-\frac{v}{\gamma}(\rho+l),$$

$$(6.1.11)\quad \log K^{*}=\log\left\{\frac{L_0}{B}\right\}+b\log\left\{\frac{\rho+l+\lambda s}{\lambda(\rho+l)}\right\}$$
$$-\frac{1}{\beta}\{a+l-(1-u)(\rho+l)\},$$

(6.1.12) $$\log Y^* = \log\left\{\frac{L_0}{B}\right\} + (b-1)\log\left\{\frac{\rho+l+\lambda s}{\lambda(\rho+l)}\right\} - \frac{1}{\beta}\{a+l-(1-u)(\rho+l)\}.$$

It follows from (5.1.4), (6.1.8), (6.1.9), (6.1.11) and (6.1.12) that the equilibrium growth path of employment is given by

(6.1.13) $$L = L^* e^{lt}$$

where $$\log L^* = \log L_0 - \frac{1}{\beta}\{a+l-(1-u)(\rho+l)\}.$$

Thus it is unrelated to the optimum path. Indeed, a comparison of (5.1.28) and (6.1.13) shows that the equilibrium growth path of employment is identical with that obtained by holding the money supply constant. This is an unsatisfactory consequence of the policy represented by (6.1.1). We must next consider the effect of the policy on the stability of the system.

From equations (6.1.4) to (6.1.6) and (6.1.10) to (6.1.12) we obtain

(6.1.14) $$Dy_1 = -\beta(b-1)y_2 + \beta b y_3,$$

(6.1.15) $$Dy_2 = -\frac{\gamma}{v}y_1 - \frac{\gamma}{v}\{v-(1+\theta)(b-1)\}y_2 + \frac{\gamma}{v}\{1+v-u-(1+\theta)b\}y_3,$$

(6.1.16) $$Dy_3 = \left\{\frac{\rho+l+\lambda s}{\rho+l}\right\}e^{y_2-y_3}Dy_2 + (\rho+l+\lambda s)(e^{y_2-y_3}-1)$$
$$= \left\{\frac{\rho+l+\lambda s}{\rho+l}\right\}\left[-\frac{\gamma}{v}y_1 - \frac{\gamma}{v}\{v-(1+\theta)(b-1)\}y_2 + \frac{\gamma}{v}\{1+v-u-(1+\theta)b\}y_3\right]e^{y_2-y_3} + (\rho+l+\lambda s)(e^{y_2-y_3}-1),$$

where $$y_1 = \log\,[w/w^* e^{\{(1-u)(\rho+l)-l\}t}],$$
$$y_2 = \log\{K/K^* e^{(\rho+l)t}\},$$
$$y_3 = \log\{Y/Y^* e^{(\rho+l)t}\}.$$

The exact paths of the y_i's are determined by their initial values and the above system, and the approximate paths by the initial values and the linear system comprising equations (6.1.14), (6.1.15) and

(6.1.17) $$Dy_3 = -\frac{\gamma}{v}\left\{\frac{\rho+l+\lambda s}{\rho+l}\right\}y_1 + (\rho+l+\lambda s)\left\{1-\frac{\gamma\{v-(1+\theta)(b-1)\}}{v(\rho+l)}\right\}y_2 + (\rho+l+\lambda s)\left\{\frac{\gamma\{1+v-u-(1+\theta)b\}}{v(\rho+l)}-1\right\}y_3.$$

The characteristic roots of the matrix of coefficients of the latter system are the roots of

$$x^3 + a_1x^2 + a_2x + a_3 = 0, \tag{6.1.18}$$

where

$$a_1 = \rho + l + \lambda s + \frac{\gamma}{v}(u + \theta) + \frac{\gamma\lambda s}{v(\rho + l)}\{b(1 + \theta) + u - v - 1\},$$

$$a_2 = \frac{\gamma}{v}(u + \theta)(\rho + l + \lambda s) + \frac{\gamma\beta}{v}\left(1 + \frac{b\lambda s}{\rho + l}\right),$$

$$a_3 = \frac{\gamma\beta}{v}(\rho + l + \lambda s).$$

We note that $a_3 > 0$, $\frac{\partial a_1}{\partial\theta} > 0$ and, provided that $a_1 > 0$, $\frac{\partial(a_1a_2 - a_3)}{\partial\theta} > 0$. Hence, although the policy represented by (6.1.1) has no effect (as compared with a policy of holding the money supply constant) on the equilibrium growth path of employment, it can have a stabilising influence.

Suppose, for example, that $\rho = 0{\cdot}04$, $l = 0{\cdot}01$, $s = 0{\cdot}20$, $b = 1{\cdot}50$, $\lambda = 4{\cdot}00$, $\gamma = 0{\cdot}20$, $\beta = 2{\cdot}00$, $u = 1{\cdot}00$ and $v = 1{\cdot}00$. Then, if $\theta = 0{\cdot}00$, the roots of (6.1.18) are: $-0{\cdot}034$, $-1{\cdot}31 \pm (2{\cdot}89)i$ while, if $\theta = 1{\cdot}00$, they are $-0{\cdot}034$, $-1{\cdot}70$, $-5{\cdot}92$. Hence the effect of the monetary policy, in this case, is to eliminate the cycle and cause a more rapid convergence to the long-term trend.

We consider, next, the policy represented by

$$D \log M_s = \theta \log \left\{\frac{\hat{L}e^{lt}}{L}\right\}. \tag{6.1.19}$$

This implies that, when employment is at the optimum level, the money supply is held constant and that, otherwise, the proportional rate of increase in the money supply is an increasing function of the proportional excess of $\hat{L}e^{lt}$ over L. The model now comprises equations (5.1.1) to (5.1.9) and (6.1.19).

From (5.1.7), (5.1.8) and (5.1.12) we obtain

$$D \log K = \gamma\left(1 - \frac{u}{v}\right) \log Y - \gamma \log K - \frac{\gamma}{v} \log p + \frac{\gamma}{v} \log M_s + \gamma\left[\log \left\{\frac{b(1 + \pi) - 1}{b(1 + \pi)(1 + c)}\right\} - \frac{1}{v} \log A\right], \tag{6.1.20}$$

which, together with (5.1.4) and (5.1.5), yields

$$D \log K = \frac{\gamma}{v}(1 + v - u - b) \log Y - \frac{\gamma}{v}(1 + v - b) \log K + \frac{\gamma}{v} \log \left\{\frac{M_s}{w}\right\} + \frac{\gamma\rho t}{v} + \frac{\gamma}{v}\left[v \log \left\{\frac{b(1 + \pi) - 1}{b(1 + \pi)(1 + c)}\right\} - \log \{b(1 + \pi)AB\}\right]. \tag{6.1.21}$$

And, from (5.1.4) and (6.1.19) we obtain

$$(6.1.22)\quad D \log M_s = \theta(b-1)\log K - \theta\, b \log Y + \theta(\rho + l)t + \theta \log \left\{\frac{\hat{L}}{B}\right\}$$

which, together with (6.1.5), yields

$$(6.1.23)\quad D \log \left\{\frac{M_s}{w}\right\} = (b-1)(\beta+\theta)\log K - b(\beta+\theta)\log Y + (\beta+\theta)(\rho+l)t + \beta \log\left\{\frac{L_0}{B}\right\} + \theta \log\left\{\frac{\hat{L}}{B}\right\} - a.$$

The paths of $\frac{M_s}{w}$, K and Y are determined by their initial values and the system comprising equations (6.1.6), (6.1.21) and (6.1.23). (The separate paths of M_s and w could then be obtained by using (6.1.5) and (6.1.22).) This system has a particular solution

$$(6.1.24)\quad \frac{M_s}{w} = \left\{\frac{M_s}{w}\right\}^* e^{\{l-(1-u)(\rho+l)\}t},$$

$$(6.1.25)\quad K = K^* e^{(\rho+l)t},$$

$$(6.1.26)\quad Y = Y^* e^{(\rho+l)t},$$

where

$$(6.1.27)\quad \log\left\{\frac{M_s}{w}\right\}^* = \frac{u}{\beta+\theta}\left[\beta \log\left\{\frac{L_0}{B}\right\} + \theta \log\left\{\frac{\hat{L}}{B}\right\} + (1-u)(\rho+l) - l - a\right] + \{v - (1-u)(b-1)\}\log\left\{\frac{\rho+l+\lambda s}{\lambda(\rho+l)}\right\} - v \log\left\{\frac{b(1+\pi)-1}{b(1+\pi)(1+c)}\right\} + \log\{b(1+\pi)AB\} + \frac{v}{\gamma}(\rho+l),$$

$$(6.1.28)\quad \log K^* = \frac{1}{\beta+\theta}\left[\beta \log\left\{\frac{L_0}{B}\right\} + \theta \log\left\{\frac{\hat{L}}{B}\right\} + (1-u)(\rho+l) - l - a\right] + b \log\left\{\frac{\rho+l+\lambda s}{(\rho+l)}\right\},$$

$$(6.1.29)\quad \log Y^* = \frac{1}{\beta+\theta}\left[\beta \log\left\{\frac{L_0}{B}\right\} + \theta \log\left\{\frac{\hat{L}}{B}\right\} + (1-u)(\rho+l) - l - a\right] + (b-1)\log\left\{\frac{\rho+l+\lambda s}{\lambda(\rho+l)}\right\}.$$

It follows from (5.1.4), (6.1.25), (6.1.26), (6.1.28) and (6.1.29) that the equilibrium growth path of employment is given by

$$L = L^* e^{lt} \tag{6.1.30}$$

where

$$\log L^* = \frac{1}{\beta + \theta}\{\beta \log L_0 + \theta \log \hat{L} + (1 - u)(\rho + l) - a - l\}.$$

Moreover, we have

$$\log \left\{\frac{L^*}{L_0}\right\} = \frac{1}{\beta + \theta}\left[\theta \log \left\{\frac{\hat{L}}{L_0}\right\} + (1 - u)(\rho + l) - a - l\right]. \tag{6.1.31}$$

The interpretation of (6.1.31) is that the equilibrium proportional level of employment, $\frac{L^*}{L_0}$, under the policy represented by (6.1.19), is a weighted geometric mean of the optimum proportional level of employment $\frac{\hat{L}}{L_0}$ and the equilibrium proportional level of employment when the money supply is held constant (cf. (5.1.28) and (6.1.13)). The difference between $\frac{L^*}{L_0}$ and $\frac{\hat{L}}{L_0}$ is smaller, the larger is θ and tends to zero as θ tends to infinity. Thus the policy represented by (6.1.19) reduces, but does not eliminate, the difference between the equilibrium and optimum proportional levels of employment. In this respect it is superior to the policy represented by (6.1.1) but, nevertheless, unsatisfactory.

It should be noted that, under the policy represented by (6.1.19), the money supply continues to change so long as the level of employment is not optimal. It is perhaps, surprising, therefore, that the policy does not give $L^* = \hat{L}$. The explanation is that, in the steady state, the wage rate changes at a rate which exactly offsets the effect on the proportional level of employment of the changing money supply. The proportional rates of increase in the wage rate and the money supply in the steady state can easily be obtained from (6.1.5), (6.1.19), (6.1.25), (6.1.26) and (6.1.30). They are given by

$$\left\{\frac{DM_s}{M_s}\right\}^* = \frac{\theta}{\beta + \theta}\left[\beta \log \left\{\frac{\hat{L}}{L_0}\right\} + a + l - (1 - u)(\rho + l)\right], \tag{6.1.32}$$

$$\left\{\frac{Dw}{w}\right\}^* = \frac{\theta}{\beta + \theta}\left[\beta \log \left\{\frac{\hat{L}}{L_0}\right\} + a + \frac{\beta}{\theta}\{(1 - u)(\rho + l) - l\}\right]. \tag{6.1.33}$$

From (6.1.6), (6.1.21), (6.1.23) and (6.1.27) to (6.1.29) we obtain

$$Dy_1 = (b - 1)(\beta + \theta)y_2 - b(\beta + \theta)y_3, \tag{6.1.34}$$

$$Dy_2 = \frac{\gamma}{v}y_1 - \frac{\gamma}{v}(1 + v - b)y_2 + \frac{\gamma}{v}(1 + v - u - b)y_3, \tag{6.1.35}$$

$$(6.1.36)\quad Dy_3 = \left\{\frac{\rho + l + \lambda s}{\rho + l}\right\} e^{y_2 - y_3} Dy_2 + (\rho + l + \lambda s)(e^{y_2 - y_3} - 1)$$

$$= \left\{\frac{\rho + l + \lambda s}{\rho + l}\right\}\left[\frac{\gamma}{v} y_1 - \frac{\gamma}{v}(1 + v - b) y_2 + \frac{\gamma}{v}(1 + v - u - b) y_3\right] e^{y_2 - y_3}$$
$$+ (\rho + l + \lambda s)(e^{y_2 - y_3} - 1),$$

where $\quad y_1 = \log\left[\frac{M_s}{w}\bigg/\left\{\frac{M_s}{w}\right\}^* e^{\{l - (1-u)(\rho + l)\}t}\right],$

$$y_2 = \log\{K/K^* e^{(\rho + l)t}\},$$

$$y_3 = \log\{Y/Y^* e^{(\rho + l)t}\}.$$

The exact paths of the y_i's are determined by their initial values and the above system, and the approximate paths by the initial values and the system comprising equations (6.1.34), (6.1.35) and

$$(6.1.37)\quad Dy_3 = \frac{\gamma}{v}\left\{\frac{\rho + l + \lambda s}{\rho + l}\right\} y_1$$
$$+ (\rho + l + \lambda s)\left\{1 - \frac{\gamma(1 + v - b)}{v(\rho + l)}\right\} y_2$$
$$+ (\rho + l + \lambda s)\left\{\frac{\gamma(1 + v - u - b)}{v(\rho + l)} - 1\right\} y_3$$

The characteristic roots of the matrix of coefficients of the latter system are the roots of

$$(6.1.38)\qquad x^3 + a_1 x^2 + a_2 x + a_3 = 0,$$

where

$$a_1 = \rho + l + \lambda s + \frac{\gamma u}{v} + \frac{\gamma \lambda s}{v(\rho + l)}(b + u - v - 1),$$

$$a_2 = \frac{\gamma u}{v}(\rho + l + \lambda s) + \frac{\gamma(\beta + \theta)}{v}\left(1 + \frac{b \lambda s}{\rho + l}\right),$$

$$a_3 = \frac{\gamma}{v}(\beta + \theta)(\rho + l + \lambda s).$$

We note that a_1 is independent of θ, and that, even if $a_1 > 0$, $\partial(a_1 a_2 - a_3)/\partial\theta$ may be negative. These results suggest that the policy represented by (6.1.19) is less satisfactory as a stabiliser than that represented by (6.1.1).

Suppose, for example, that $\rho = 0{\cdot}04$, $l = 0{\cdot}01$, $s = 0{\cdot}20$, $b = 1{\cdot}50$, $\lambda = 4{\cdot}00$, $\gamma = 0{\cdot}20$, $\beta = 2{\cdot}00$, $u = 1{\cdot}00$ and $v = 1{\cdot}00$. Then if $\theta = 0$, the roots of (6.1.38) are: $-0{\cdot}034$, $-1{\cdot}31 \pm (2{\cdot}89)i$; while if $\theta = 2{\cdot}00$, they are: $-0{\cdot}034$, $-1{\cdot}31 \pm (4{\cdot}29)i$. Hence, in this case, the monetary policy has no significant effect on the damping of the cycle. Its main effects are to reduce the difference between the equilibrium and optimum proportional levels of employment and to reduce the period of the cycle.

We consider next the policy represented by

$$(6.1.39) \qquad D^2 \log M_s = \theta \log \left\{\frac{\hat{L}e^{lt}}{L}\right\}.$$

This implies that the proportional rate of increase in the money supply is decreasing, constant or increasing according as the actual level of employment is greater than, equal to or less than the optimum level. The model now comprises equations (5.1.1) to (5.1.9) and (6.1.39).

Let us introduce a new variable z defined by

$$(6.1.40) \qquad D \log M_s = z.$$

Then, from (6.1.5) and (6.1.40), we obtain

$$(6.1.41) \quad D \log \left\{\frac{M_s}{w}\right\} = \beta(b-1) \log K - \beta b \log Y + z + \beta(\rho + l)t - a + \beta \log \left\{\frac{L_0}{B}\right\},$$

and from (5.1.4), (6.1.39) and (6.1.40),

$$(6.1.42) \quad Dz = \theta(b-1) \log K - \theta b \log Y + \theta(\rho + l)t + \theta \log \left\{\frac{\hat{L}}{B}\right\}.$$

The paths of $\frac{M_s}{w}$, K, Y and z are determined by their initial values and the system comprising equations (6.1.6), (6.1.21), (6.1.41) and (6.1.42). This system has a particular solution

$$(6.1.43) \qquad \frac{M_s}{w} = \left\{\frac{M_s}{w}\right\}^* e^{\{l-(1-u)(\rho+l)\}t},$$

$$(6.1.44) \qquad K = K^* e^{(\rho+l)t},$$

$$(6.1.45) \qquad Y = Y^* e^{(\rho+l)t},$$

$$(6.1.46) \qquad z = z^*,$$

where:

$$(6.1.47) \quad \log \left\{\frac{M_s}{w}\right\}^* = u \log \left\{\frac{\hat{L}}{B}\right\} + \{v - (1-u)(b-1)\} \log \left\{\frac{\rho + l + \lambda s}{\lambda(\rho + l)}\right\} - v \log \left\{\frac{b(1+\pi) - 1}{b(1+\pi)(1+c)}\right\} + \log \{b(1+\pi)AB\} + \frac{v}{\gamma}(\rho + l),$$

$$(6.1.48) \quad \log K^* = \log \left\{\frac{\hat{L}}{B}\right\} + b \log \left\{\frac{\rho + l + \lambda s}{\lambda(\rho + l)}\right\},$$

(6.1.49) $\log Y^* = \log\left\{\frac{\hat{L}}{B}\right\} + (b-1)\log\left\{\frac{\rho+l+\lambda s}{\lambda(\rho+l)}\right\},$

(6.1.50) $z^* = \beta\log\left\{\frac{\hat{L}}{L_0}\right\} + a + l - (1-u)(\rho+l).$

It follows from (5.1.4), (6.1.44), (6.1.45), (6.1.48) and (6.1.49) that the equilibrium growth path of employment is given by

(6.1.51) $$L = \hat{L}e^{lt}.$$

Hence, the equilibrium and optimum paths of employment are identical. In this respect the policy represented by (6.1.39) is superior to those represented by (6.1.1) and (6.1.19).

From (6.1.6), (6.1.21), (6.1.41), (6.1.42) and (6.1.47) to (6.1.50) we obtain

(6.1.52) $Dy_1 = \beta(b-1)y_2 - \beta by_3 + y_4,$

(6.1.53) $Dy_2 = \frac{\gamma}{v}y_1 - \frac{\gamma}{v}(1+v-b)y_2 + \frac{\gamma}{v}(1+v-u-b)y_3,$

(6.1.54) $$Dy_3 = \left\{\frac{\rho+l+\lambda s}{\rho+l}\right\}e^{y_2-y_3}Dy_2 + (\rho+l+\lambda s)(e^{y_2-y_3}-1)$$
$$= \left\{\frac{\rho+l+\lambda s}{\rho+l}\right\}\left[\frac{\gamma}{v}y_1 - \frac{\gamma}{v}(1+v-b)y_2 + \frac{\gamma}{v}(1+v-u-b)y_3\right]e^{y_2-y_3} + (\rho+l+\lambda s)(e^{y_2-y_3}-1),$$

(6.1.55) $Dy_4 = \theta(b-1)y_2 - \theta by_3,$

where $y_1 = \log\left[\frac{M_s}{w}\Big/\left\{\frac{M_s}{w}\right\}^* e^{\{l-(1-u)(\rho+l)\}t}\right],$

$y_2 = \log\{K/K^*e^{(\rho+l)t}\},$

$y_3 = \log\{Y/Y^*e^{(\rho+l)t}\},$

$y_4 = z - z^*.$

The exact paths of the y_i's are determined by their initial values and the above system, and the approximate paths by the initial values and the linear system comprising equations (6.1.52), 6.1.53), (6.1.55) and

(6.1.56) $$Dy_3 = \frac{\gamma}{v}\left\{\frac{\rho+l+\lambda s}{\rho+l}\right\}y_1 + (\rho+l+\lambda s)\left\{1 - \frac{\gamma(1+v-b)}{v(\rho+l)}\right\}y_2 + (\rho+l+\lambda s)\left\{\frac{\gamma(1+v-u-b)}{v(\rho+l)} - 1\right\}y_3.$$

The characteristic roots of the matrix of coefficients of the latter system are the roots of

$$(6.1.57) \qquad x^4 + a_1x^3 + a_2x^2 + a_3x + a_4 = 0,$$

where
$$a_1 = \rho + l + \lambda s + \frac{\gamma u}{v} + \frac{\gamma\lambda s}{v(\rho + l)}(b + u - v - 1),$$
$$a_2 = \frac{\gamma u}{v}(\rho + l + \lambda s) + \frac{\gamma\beta}{v}\left(1 + \frac{b\lambda s}{\rho + l}\right),$$
$$a_3 = \frac{\beta\gamma}{v}(\rho + l + \lambda s) + \frac{\gamma\theta}{v}\left(1 + \frac{b\lambda s}{\rho + l}\right),$$
$$a_4 = \frac{\gamma\theta}{v}(\rho + l + \lambda s).$$

Necessary and sufficient conditions for these roots to have negative real parts are: $a_1 > 0$, $a_4 > 0$, $a_1a_2 - a_3 > 0$, $a_3(a_1a_2 - a_3) - a_1^2a_4 > 0$. We note that $\partial(a_1a_2 - a_3)/\partial\theta < 0$. Hence the policy represented by (6.1.39) can have a destabilising influence.

Suppose, for example, that $\rho = 0{\cdot}04$, $l = 0{\cdot}01$, $s = 0{\cdot}20$, $b = 1{\cdot}50$, $\lambda = 4{\cdot}00$, $\gamma = 0{\cdot}20$, $\beta = 2{\cdot}00$, $u = 1{\cdot}00$, $v = 1{\cdot}00$ and $\theta = 1{\cdot}00$. Then the roots of (6.1.57) are: $-0{\cdot}034$, $-0{\cdot}56$, $-1{\cdot}03 \pm (2{\cdot}80)i$. A comparison of this result with that obtained under the assumption of a constant money supply shows that, in this case, one of the effects of the monetary policy is to reduce the damping of the cycle. (We recall that the roots of (6.1.18) or (6.1.38), when $\theta = 0$, are: $-0{\cdot}034$, $-1{\cdot}31 \pm (2{\cdot}89)i$.)

The policies represented by (6.1.1), (6.1.19) and (6.1.39) are all special cases of the more general policy represented by

$$(6.1.58) \qquad D^2 \log M_s = (\theta_1D^2 + \theta_2D + \theta_3) \log \left\{\frac{\hat{L}e^{lt}}{L}\right\}.$$

Equation (6.1.1) implies that $\theta_2 = \theta_3 = 0$, (6.1.19) that $\theta_1 = \theta_3 = 0$ and (6.1.39) that $\theta_1 = \theta_2 = 0$. The most satisfactory policy of this type can be expected to involve positive values of all three policy parameters. We now consider a somewhat less general case in which $\theta_1 = 0$, $\theta_2 > 0$, $\theta_3 > 0$. Equation (6.1.58) then becomes

$$(6.1.59) \qquad D^2 \log M_s = (\theta_2D + \theta_3) \log \left\{\frac{\hat{L}e^{lt}}{L}\right\},$$

and the complete model comprises equations (5.1.1) to (5.1.9) and (6.1.59).

From (5.1.4), (6.1.40) and (6.1.59) we obtain

$$(6.1.60) \qquad Dz = \theta_2(b - 1)D \log K - \theta_2bD \log Y + \theta_3(b - 1) \log K - \theta_3b \log Y + \theta_3(\rho + l)t + \theta_3 \log \left\{\frac{\hat{L}}{B}\right\} + \theta_2(\rho + l).$$

The paths of $\frac{M_s}{w}$, K, Y and z are determined by their initial values and the system comprising equations (6.1.6), (6.1.21), (6.1.41) and (6.1.60). The equilibrium growth paths of these variables are again given by (6.1.43) to (6.1.50), and the equilibrium growth path of employment by (6.1.51). Thus the equilibrium and optimum paths of employment are identical. This result will, indeed, be obtained under any policy that can be represented by (6.1.58) provided that $\theta_3 > 0$.

From (6.1.60) and (6.1.48) to (6.1.50) we obtain

$$(6.1.61)\quad Dy_4 = \theta_2(b-1)Dy_2 - \theta_2 bDy_3 + \theta_3(b-1)y_2 - \theta_3 by_3,$$

where the y_i's are as previously defined. And, as before, we have (6.1.52), (6.1.53) and (6.1.54). From (6.1.53), (6.1.54) and (6.1.61) we obtain

$$(6.1.62)\quad Dy_4 = \frac{\theta_2\gamma}{v}(b-1)y_1 + (b-1)\left\{\theta_3 - \frac{\theta_2\gamma}{v}(1+v-b)\right\}y_2$$
$$+\left\{\frac{\theta_2\gamma}{v}(b-1)(1+v-u-b) - \theta_3 b\right\}y_3 - \theta_2 b(\rho+l+\lambda s)(e^{y_2-y_3}-1)$$
$$-\theta_2 b\left\{\frac{\rho+l+\lambda s}{\rho+l}\right\}\left[\frac{\gamma}{v}y_1 - \frac{\gamma}{v}(1+v-b)y_2 + \frac{\gamma}{v}(1+v-u-b)y_3\right]e^{y_2-y_3}.$$

The exact paths of the y_i's are determined by their initial values and equations (6.1.52), (6.1.53), (6.1.54) and (6.1.62), and their approximate paths by the initial values and the linear system comprising equations (6.1.52), (6.1.53), (6.1.56) and

$$(6.1.63)\quad Dy_4 = -\frac{\theta_2\gamma}{v}\left(1+\frac{b\lambda s}{\rho+l}\right)y_1$$
$$+\left\{\frac{\theta_2\gamma}{v}(1+v-b)\left(1+\frac{b\lambda s}{\rho+l}\right) - \theta_2 b(\rho+l+\lambda s) + \theta_3(b-1)\right\}y_2$$
$$-\left\{\frac{\theta_2\gamma}{v}(1+v-u-b)\left(1+\frac{b\lambda s}{\rho+l}\right) - \theta_2 b(\rho+l+\lambda s) + \theta_3 b\right\}y_3.$$

Suppose, for example, that $\rho = 0{\cdot}04$, $l = 0{\cdot}01$, $s = 0{\cdot}20$, $b = 1{\cdot}50$, $\lambda = 4{\cdot}00$, $\gamma = 0{\cdot}20$, $\beta = 2{\cdot}00$, $u = 1{\cdot}00$, $v = 1{\cdot}00$, $\theta_2 = 1{\cdot}00$ and $\theta_3 = 1{\cdot}00$. Then the approximate linear system is

$$(6.1.64)\quad Dy = Fy,$$

where

$$y = \begin{bmatrix} y_1 \\ y_2 \\ y_3 \\ y_4 \end{bmatrix},\quad F = \begin{bmatrix} 0{\cdot}00 & 1{\cdot}00 & -3{\cdot}00 & 1{\cdot}00 \\ 0{\cdot}20 & -0{\cdot}10 & -0{\cdot}10 & 0{\cdot}00 \\ 3{\cdot}40 & -0{\cdot}85 & -2{\cdot}55 & 0{\cdot}00 \\ -5{\cdot}00 & 1{\cdot}73 & 2{\cdot}27 & 0{\cdot}00 \end{bmatrix}.$$

The characteristic roots of F are: $-0{\cdot}034$, $-0{\cdot}35$, $-1{\cdot}14 \pm (3{\cdot}59)i$. Thus, as compared with the case in which $\theta_2 = 0$ and $\theta_3 = 1{\cdot}00$, the damping of the cycle is increased but its period is reduced.

6.2 Fiscal Policy

Government expenditure and taxation have not been formally introduced into the model under discussion. But C can be identified with the sum of real private consumption and real government current expenditure on goods and services, while K can be identified with the sum of government and private fixed capital. Equation (5.1.1) then implies that sY equals the sum of real private and government saving, the latter being the excess of real taxation receipts over real government current expenditure on goods and services. And the parameter s then depends on three ratios: (1) the ratio of private consumption to private disposable income, (2) the ratio of taxation receipts to income (i.e. the average rate of taxation), (3) the ratio of government current expenditure on goods and services to taxation receipts. So far we have implicitly assumed that each of these ratios is constant. We shall now assume that the second and third ratios are varied in response to changes in the proportional level of employment. Thus s will now be treated as a variable rather than a parameter.

We assume, in particular, that

$$(6.2.1) \qquad s = \epsilon_1 + \epsilon_2 \log \left\{\frac{L}{\hat{L}e^{lt}}\right\},$$

where ϵ_1 and ϵ_2 are positive constants. The complete model then comprises equations (5.1.1) to (5.1.10) and (6.2.1). From (5.1.4) and (6.2.1) we obtain

$$(6.2.2) \qquad s = \epsilon_1 + \epsilon_2 b \log Y - \epsilon_2(b-1)\log K - \epsilon_2(\rho + l)t + \epsilon_2 \log \left\{\frac{B}{\hat{L}}\right\},$$

which, together with (5.1.17), yields

$$(6.2.3) \qquad D \log Y = \lambda\left\{\frac{K}{Y}\right\} D \log K + \lambda\epsilon_2(b-1)\log K - \lambda\epsilon_2 b \log Y + \lambda\epsilon_2(\rho + l)t - \lambda\epsilon_2 \log\left\{\frac{B}{\hat{L}}\right\} - \lambda\epsilon_1.$$

We also have

$$(6.2.4) \qquad D \log w = \beta b \log Y - \beta(b-1)\log K - \beta(\rho + l)t + a + \beta \log\left\{\frac{L_0}{B}\right\},$$

(6.2.5) $$D \log K = \frac{\gamma}{v}(1 + v - u - b) \log Y - \frac{\gamma}{v}(1 + v - b) \log K - \frac{\gamma}{v} \log w + \frac{\gamma}{v}(m + \rho)t + \frac{\gamma}{v}\left[v \log \left\{\frac{b(1 + \pi) - 1}{b(1 + \pi)(1 + c)}\right\} + \log \left\{\frac{M_0}{b(1 + \pi)AB}\right\}\right],$$

which are identical with (5.1.16) and (5.1.15) respectively.

The paths of w, K and Y are determined by their initial values and the system comprising equations (6.2.3) to (6.2.5). This system has a particular solution:

(6.2.6) $$w = w^* e^{\{(1-u)(\rho+l)+m-l\}t},$$

(6.2.7) $$K = K^* e^{(\rho+l)t},$$

(6.2.8) $$Y = Y^* e^{(\rho+l)t},$$

where

(6.2.9) $$\log w^* = \log \left\{\frac{M_0}{b(1 + \pi)AB}\right\} - u \log \left\{\frac{L_0}{B}\right\} + v \log \left\{\frac{b(1 + \pi) - 1}{b(1 + \pi)(1 + c)}\right\} - \{v - (1 - u)(b - 1)\} \log q + \frac{u}{\beta}\{a + l - m - (1 - u)(\rho + l)\} - \frac{v}{\gamma}(\rho + l),$$

(6.2.10) $$\log K^* = \log \left\{\frac{L_0}{B}\right\} - \frac{1}{\beta}\{a + l - m - (1 - u)(\rho + l)\} + b \log q,$$

(6.2.11) $$\log Y^* = \log \left\{\frac{L_0}{B}\right\} - \frac{1}{\beta}\{a + l - m - (1 - u)(\rho + l)\} + (b - 1) \log q,$$

(6.2.12) $$q = \frac{K^*}{Y^*} = \frac{\rho + l + \lambda\epsilon_1}{\lambda(\rho + l)} - \frac{\epsilon_2}{\beta(\rho + l)}\{a + l - m - (1 - u)(\rho + l)\} + \frac{\epsilon_2}{\rho + l} \log \left\{\frac{L_0}{\hat{L}}\right\}.$$

It follows from (5.1.4), (6.2.7), (6.2.8), (6.2.10) and (6.2.11) that the equilibrium growth path of employment is given by

(6.2.13) $$L = L^* e^{lt},$$

where $$\log L^* = \log L_0 - \frac{1}{\beta}\{a + l - m - (1 - u)(\rho + l)\}.$$

We note that (6.2.13) is identical with (5.1.28), L^* being independent of $\hat{L}$, ϵ_1 and ϵ_2. Hence the equilibrium growth path of employment is independent of the optimum path and unaffected by the fiscal policy represented by (6.2.1). The policy, nevertheless, affects the equilibrium growth path of output. Indeed, it is clear from (6.2.11) that $\frac{\partial Y^*}{\partial \epsilon_1} > 0$. The explanation of this result is that an increase in the taxation rate (associated with a decrease in government borrowing from the private sector) or a decrease in the proportion of taxation receipts devoted to current government expenditure increases the equilibrium ratio of capital to output.

From equations (6.2.3) to (6.2.5) and (6.2.9) to (6.2.12) we obtain

$$(6.2.14)\quad Dy_1 = -\beta(b-1)y_2 + \beta b y_3,$$

$$(6.2.15)\quad Dy_2 = -\frac{\gamma}{v}y_1 - \frac{\gamma}{v}(1+v-b)y_2 + \frac{\gamma}{v}(1+v-u-b)y_3,$$

$$\begin{aligned}(6.2.16)\quad Dy_3 &= \lambda q e^{y_2-y_3}Dy_2 + \lambda\epsilon_2(b-1)y_2 - \lambda\epsilon_2 b y_3 \\ &\quad + \lambda q(\rho+l)(e^{y_2-y_3}-1) \\ &= \lambda q\left\{-\frac{\gamma}{v}y_1 - \frac{\gamma}{v}(1+v-b)y_2 + \frac{\gamma}{v}(1+v-u-b)y_3\right\}e^{y_2-y_3} \\ &\quad + \lambda\epsilon_2(b-1)y_2 - \lambda\epsilon_2 b y_3 + \lambda q(\rho+l)(e^{y_2-y_3}-1),\end{aligned}$$

where
$$y_1 = \log\{w/w^* e^{\{(1-u)(\rho+l)+m-l\}t}\},$$
$$y_2 = \log\{K/K^* e^{(\rho+l)t}\},$$
$$y_3 = \log\{Y/Y^* e^{(\rho+l)t}\}.$$

The exact paths of the y_i's are determined by their initial values and the above system, and the approximate paths by the initial values and the linear system comprising equations (6.2.14), (6.2.15) and

$$\begin{aligned}(6.2.17)\quad Dy_3 = -\frac{\gamma\lambda q}{v}y_1 &+ \lambda q\left\{\rho + l + \frac{\epsilon_2}{q}(b-1) - \frac{\gamma}{v}(1+v-b)\right\}y_2 \\ &+ \lambda q\left\{\frac{\gamma}{v}(1+v-u-b) - \rho - l - \frac{\epsilon_2 b}{q}\right\}y_3.\end{aligned}$$

The characteristic roots of the matrix of coefficients of the latter system are the roots of

$$(6.2.18)\qquad x^3 + a_1x^2 + a_2x + a_3 = 0,$$

where
$$a_1 = \frac{\gamma}{v}(1+v-b) + \lambda q\left\{\rho + l + \frac{\epsilon_2 b}{q} - \frac{\gamma}{v}(1+v-u-b)\right\},$$
$$a_2 = \frac{\beta\gamma}{v}(1-b+b\lambda q) + \frac{\gamma\lambda}{v}\{qu(\rho+l) + \epsilon_2(1+v-u-b+ub)\},$$
$$a_3 = \frac{\beta\gamma\lambda q}{v}(\rho+l).$$

The feed-back relation (6.2.1) involves two policy parameters, ϵ_1 and ϵ_2. The values of these parameters affect not only the stability of the system but also the equilibrium capital–output ratio. Let us assume, for simplicity, that the desired value of q (which is the equilibrium ratio of fixed capital to output) is determined as a separate policy decision, having regard to the fact that the equilibrium growth path of output will be higher, and the initial level of consumption lower, the greater is q. Thus, when considering the effect of a change in ϵ_2 on the stability of the system, we shall assume that ϵ_1 is changed in such a way as to hold q constant; and, when differentiating functions of the a_i's with respect to ϵ_2, the partial derivative sign will be used to indicate that q, and not ϵ_1, is constant. Then, assuming that $u > 1 - \frac{v}{b-1}$, we have $\partial a_1/\partial\epsilon_2 > 0$, $\partial a_2/\partial\epsilon_2 > 0$ and, provided that $a_1 > 0$ and $a_2 > 0$, $\partial(a_1a_2 - a_3)/\partial\epsilon_2 > 0$. Hence, a positive value of ϵ_2 can have a stabilising influence.

Suppose, for example, that $\rho = 0{\cdot}04$, $l = 0{\cdot}01$, $q = 3{\cdot}00$, $b = 1{\cdot}50$, $\lambda = 4{\cdot}00$, $\gamma = 0{\cdot}20$, $\beta = 2{\cdot}00$, $u = 1{\cdot}00$ and $v = 1{\cdot}00$. Then if $\epsilon_2 = 0$ the roots of (6.2.18) are: $-0{\cdot}034$, $-0{\cdot}93 \pm (2{\cdot}49)i$, while if $\epsilon_2 = 1$ they are: $-0{\cdot}034$, $-1{\cdot}13$, $-6{\cdot}73$. Hence, in this case, the fiscal policy eliminates the cycle and causes a more rapid convergence to the long-term trend.

We shall not consider more complicated fiscal policies analogous to the monetary policies represented by equations (6.1.19) and (6.1.39). For we assume that the only practicable fiscal policies are those for which the ratio of saving (private plus government) to the national income tends to a positive constant as $t \longrightarrow \infty$. If this assumption is correct, no practicable fiscal policy can influence the equilibrium growth path of employment. Although this conclusion is clear from (6.2.13) and the preceding argument, it may be surprising, especially when compared with the results obtained for models in which monetary phenomena are ignored (see section 3.4). We shall conclude this section, therefore, with a non-mathematical description of the effects of a change in fiscal policy that causes a permanent increase in the saving–income ratio. It will be assumed, for this purpose, that the economy is initially on its equilibrium growth path.

It should be remembered that we have assumed, in this section, that the money supply increases at a constant proportional rate and is, therefore, unaffected by fiscal changes. This implies that the excess of taxation receipts over government current expenditure is used to reduce government borrowing from the private sector of the economy and not to reduce the money supply. A change of fiscal policy of the sort referred to above, nevertheless, causes an immediate decrease in consumption and, therefore, in employment. The decrease in employment causes a decrease in the proportional rate of increase in wages and prices and, therefore, a decrease in the proportional rate of increase in the demand for money. Since the proportional rate of increase in the supply of money does not change, the interest rate gradually falls and induces a gradual increase in the demand for capital goods and the level of employment. Provided that v is not too large, the level of employment converges to its equilibrium and, in this case, initial level. Thus the only long-run effect of the change in fiscal policy is to increase the ratio of capital formation to consumption, and, hence, raise the equilibrium growth path of output.

The above description has been simplified by ignoring the time-lag in the adjustment of production to demand. Because of this lag the path of convergence will normally be oscillatory rather than steady.

6.3 The Combination of Monetary and Fiscal Policy

In the preceding sections we have distinguished three policy objectives: (1) to obtain the optimum long-run balance between unemployment and inflation, (2) to obtain the optimum long-run balance between consumption and capital formation, (3) to minimise short-term fluctuations. We have shown that, under the assumptions of the model, a monetary policy can help to achieve objectives (1) and (3), but not (2), while a fiscal policy, of the class considered to be practicable, can help to achieve objectives (2) and (3), but not (1). Hence, if all three objectives are to be pursued, a combination of monetary and fiscal policy must be used.

A powerful system of regulation can be obtained by combining the policies represented by equations (6.1.58) and (6.2.1). For simplicity we consider the combined policy represented by (6.1.39) and (6.2.1). The model now comprises equations (5.1.1) to (5.1.9), (6.1.39) and (6.2.1).

As in section 6.1 we obtain

$$(6.3.1)\quad D\log K = \frac{\gamma}{v}(1+v-u-b)\log Y - \frac{\gamma}{v}(1+v-b)\log K + \frac{\gamma}{v}\log\left\{\frac{M_s}{w}\right\} + \frac{\gamma\rho t}{v} + \frac{\gamma}{v}\left[v\log\left\{\frac{b(1+\pi)-1}{b(1+\pi)(1+c)}\right\} - \log\{b(1+\pi)AB\}\right],$$

$$(6.3.2)\quad D\log\left\{\frac{M_s}{w}\right\} = \beta(b-1)\log K - \beta b\log Y + z + \beta(\rho+l)t - a + \beta\log\left\{\frac{L_0}{B}\right\},$$

$$(6.3.3)\quad Dz = \theta(b-1)\log K - \theta b\log Y + \theta(\rho+l)t + \log\left\{\frac{\hat{L}}{B}\right\},$$

which are identical with (6.1.21), (6.1.41) and (6.1.42), respectively. And, as in section 6.2, we obtain

$$(6.3.4)\quad D\log Y = \lambda\left\{\frac{K}{Y}\right\} D\log K + \lambda\epsilon_2(b-1)\log K - \lambda\epsilon_2 b\log Y + \lambda\epsilon_2(\rho+l)t - \lambda\epsilon_2\log\left\{\frac{B}{\hat{L}}\right\} - \lambda\epsilon_1,$$

which is identical with (6.2.3).

The paths of $\frac{M_s}{w}$, K, Y and z are determined by their initial values and the system comprising equations (6.3.1) to (6.3.4). This system has a particular solution:

$$(6.3.5)\quad \frac{M_s}{w} = \left\{\frac{M_s}{w}\right\}^* e^{\{l-(1-u)(\rho+l)\}t},$$

$$(6.3.6)\quad K = K^* e^{(\rho+l)t},$$

$$(6.3.7)\quad Y = Y^* e^{(\rho+l)t},$$

$$(6.3.8)\quad z = z^*,$$

where

$$(6.3.9)\quad \log\left\{\frac{M_s}{w}\right\}^* = u\log\left\{\frac{\hat{L}}{B}\right\} + \{v-(1-u)(b-1)\}\log\left\{\frac{\rho+l+\lambda\epsilon_1}{\lambda(\rho+l)}\right\} - v\log\left\{\frac{b(1+\pi)-1}{b(1+\pi)(1+c)}\right\} + \log\{b(1+\pi)AB\} + \frac{v}{\gamma}(\rho+l),$$

$$(6.3.10)\quad \log K^* = \log\left\{\frac{\hat{L}}{B}\right\} + b\log\left\{\frac{\rho+l+\lambda\epsilon_1}{\lambda(\rho+l)}\right\},$$

$$(6.3.11)\quad \log Y^* = \log\left\{\frac{\hat{L}}{B}\right\} + (b-1)\log\left\{\frac{\rho+l+\lambda\epsilon_1}{\lambda(\rho+l)}\right\},$$

$$(6.3.12)\quad z^* = \beta\log\left\{\frac{\hat{L}}{L_0}\right\} + a + l - (1-u)(\rho+l).$$

It follows from (5.1.4), (6.3.6), (6.3.7), (6.3.10) and (6.3.11) that the equilibrium growth path of employment is given by

$$(6.3.13)\quad L = \hat{L}e^{lt}.$$

Thus, the equilibrium and optimum paths of employment are identical. Moreover, from (6.3.10) and (6.3.11), we have

$$(6.3.14)\quad \frac{K^*}{Y^*} = \frac{\rho+l+\lambda\epsilon_1}{\lambda(\rho+l)}.$$

Hence the equilibrium ratio of fixed capital to output depends on ϵ_1, but is independent of ϵ_2. It is independent of ϵ_2 because of the equality between the equilibrium and optimum proportional levels of employment.

The above results show that, by using the combined monetary and fiscal policy represented by equations (6.1.39) and (6.2.1), the equilibrium proportional level of employment and the equilibrium ratio of fixed capital to output can be controlled independently and are independent of ϵ_2. We shall now consider the relation between the stability of the system and the value of ϵ_2.

From equations (6.3.1) to (6.3.4) and (6.3.9) to (6.3.12) we obtain

$$(6.3.15)\quad Dy_1 = \beta(b-1)y_2 - \beta b y_3 + y_4,$$

$$(6.3.16)\quad Dy_2 = \frac{\gamma}{v}y_1 - \frac{\gamma}{v}(1+v-b)y_2 + \frac{\gamma}{v}(1+v-u-b)y_3,$$

$$(6.3.17)\quad Dy_3 = \left\{\frac{\rho+l+\lambda\epsilon_1}{\rho+l}\right\}e^{y_2-y_3}Dy_2 + (\rho+l+\lambda\epsilon_1)(e^{y_2-y_3}-1)$$
$$+\lambda\epsilon_2(b-1)y_2 - \lambda\epsilon_2 b y_3 = \left\{\frac{\rho+l+\lambda\epsilon_1}{\rho+l}\right\}\left\{\frac{\gamma}{v}y_1\right.$$
$$\left.-\frac{\gamma}{v}(1+v-b)y_2 + \frac{\gamma}{v}(1+v-u-b)y_3\right\}e^{y_2-y_3}$$
$$+(\rho+l+\lambda\epsilon_1)(e^{y_2-y_3}-1) + \lambda\epsilon_2(b-1)y_2 - \lambda\epsilon_2 b y_3,$$

$$(6.3.18)\quad Dy_4 = \theta(b-1)y_2 - \theta b y_3,$$

where $\quad y_1 = \log\left[\frac{M_s}{w}\Big/\left\{\frac{M_s}{w}\right\}^* e^{\{l-(1-u)(\rho+l)\}t}\right],$

$$y_2 = \log\{K/K^*e^{(\rho+l)t}\},$$

$$y_3 = \log\{Y/Y^*e^{(\rho+l)t}\},$$

$$y_4 = z - z^*.$$

The exact paths of the y_i's are determined by their initial values and the above system, and the approximate paths by the initial values and the system comprising equations (6.3.15), (6.3.16), (6.3.18) and

$$(6.3.19)\quad Dy_3 = \frac{\gamma}{v}\left\{\frac{\rho+l+\lambda\epsilon_1}{\rho+l}\right\}y_1$$
$$+\left[(\rho+l+\lambda\epsilon_1)\left\{1-\frac{\gamma(1+v-b)}{v(\rho+l)}\right\}+\lambda\epsilon_2(b-1)\right]y_2$$
$$+\left[(\rho+l+\lambda\epsilon_1)\left\{\frac{\gamma(1+v-u-b)}{v(\rho+l)}-1\right\}-\lambda\epsilon_2 b\right]y_3.$$

The characteristic roots of the matrix of coefficients of the latter system are the roots of

$$x^4 + a_1x^3 + a_2x^2 + a_3x + a_4 = 0, \tag{6.3.20}$$

where

$$a_1 = \rho + l + \lambda\epsilon_1 + \frac{\gamma u}{v} + \frac{\gamma\lambda\epsilon_1}{v(\rho + l)}(b + u - v - 1) + \lambda\epsilon_2 b,$$

$$a_2 = \frac{\gamma u}{v}(\rho + l + \lambda\epsilon_1) + \frac{\gamma\beta}{v}\left\{1 + \frac{b\lambda\epsilon_1}{\rho + l}\right\} + \frac{\gamma\lambda\epsilon_2}{v}(1 + v - u - b + ub),$$

$$a_3 = \frac{\beta\gamma}{v}(\rho + l + \lambda\epsilon_1) + \frac{\gamma\theta}{v}\left(1 + \frac{b\lambda\epsilon_1}{\rho + l}\right),$$

$$a_4 = \frac{\gamma\theta}{v}(\rho + l + \lambda\epsilon_1).$$

We note that $a_4 > 0$ and $\partial a_1/\partial\epsilon_2 > 0$. Moreover, provided that $u > 1 - \dfrac{v}{b - 1}$ and $a_1 > 0$, we have $\partial(a_1a_2 - a_3)/\partial\epsilon_2 > 0$ while, if, in addition, θ is sufficiently small, we have $\partial(a_1a_2a_3 - a_3^2 - a_1^2a_4)/\partial\epsilon_2 > 0$. Hence a positive ϵ_2 can have a stabilising influence.

Suppose, for example, that $\rho = 0{\cdot}04$, $l = 0{\cdot}01$, $b = 1{\cdot}50$, $\lambda = 4{\cdot}00$, $\gamma = 0{\cdot}20$, $\beta = 2{\cdot}00$, $u = 1{\cdot}00$, $v = 1{\cdot}00$, $\epsilon_1 = 0{\cdot}20$ and $\theta = 1{\cdot}00$. Then, if $\epsilon_2 = 0$ the roots of (6.3.20) are: $-0{\cdot}034$, $-0{\cdot}56$, $-1{\cdot}03 \pm (2{\cdot}80)i$, while if $\epsilon_2 = 0{\cdot}50$ they are: $-0{\cdot}034$, $-0{\cdot}74$, $-2{\cdot}44 \pm (0{\cdot}90)i$. Hence, in this case, the effect of a positive ϵ_2 is to increase both the period and damping of the cycle and give a more rapid convergence to the long-term trend.

CHAPTER 7

THE TREATMENT OF TECHNICAL PROGRESS

IN the models discussed in Chapters 4 to 6 technical progress was allowed for by including a trend term in the production function. Thus the amount of labour employed was assumed to be a function of output, the amount of capital, and time. Some of the most important recent contributions to economic model building have been concerned with more realistic ways of allowing for technical progress.

These developments are based on two ideas. The first is that new technical knowledge may have little influence on productivity until it has been embodied in new types of durable equipment. Hence our models should distinguish between different vintages of capital (i.e. capital produced at different points of time). The second is that the rate of accumulation of technical knowledge is itself dependent on economic variables. It should, therefore, be treated as an endogenous variable and explained by the model.

Models involving one or both of these ideas will be discussed in the first three sections of this chapter. In the final section we shall reconsider the usefulness, as tools of prediction, of models involving the type of production function used in Chapters 4 to 6.

7.1 Embodied Technical Progress with Ex-post Substitution

The ratio of labour to capital used in the production of a given output can be varied in two ways: (1) by varying the type of equipment used, (2) by varying the intensity with which a given type of equipment is used. If the ratio of labour to capital is decided before the equipment is purchased (or built) both types of variation can be allowed for and, in this case, we refer to the possible variation in the labour–capital ratio as *ex-ante substitution* between labour and capital. But, if the ratio of labour to capital is decided after the equipment is purchased, only the latter type of variation can be allowed for, and in this case we refer to *ex-post substitution* between the factors.

Generally we must expect both the ex-ante and ex-post elasticities of substitution between labour and capital to be negative (rather than zero) and the modulus of the ex-post elasticity to be less than that of the ex-ante elasticity. But, so far, the literature has been confined to two limiting cases: (1) where the ex-ante and ex-post elasticities of substitution are equal, (2) where the ex-post elasticity of substitution is zero.

We shall now consider a model in which the ex-ante and ex-post elasticities of substitution are equal, each being -1. The model, which is due to Solow (1960) is:

(7.1.1) $L_v(t) = Be^{-\rho v}\{Q_v(t)\}^b\{K_v(t)\}^{1-b}$ $\qquad (v \leq t)$

(7.1.2) $K_v(t) = I(v)e^{-\delta(t-v)},$ $\qquad (v \leq t)$

(7.1.3) $C(t) = (1 - s)Q(t),$

(7.1.4) $w(t)\dfrac{\partial L_v(t)}{\partial Q_v(t)} = p(t),$ $\qquad (v \leq t)$

(7.1.5) $Q(t) = \int_{-\infty}^{t} Q_v(t)\, dv,$

(7.1.6) $L(t) = \int_{-\infty}^{t} L_v(t)\, dv,$

(7.1.7) $L_s(t) = L_0e^{lt},$

(7.1.8) $Q(t) = C(t) + I(t),$

(7.1.9) $L(t) = L_s(t),$

where

$K_v(t)$ = amount of capital of vintage v still in existence at time t, or, more precisely, $\lim_{h\to 0} \frac{1}{h}$\{amount of capital produced in the time interval $(v, v + h)$ and still in existence at time t\},

$Q_v(t)$ = output at time t produced with capital of vintage v, or, more precisely, $\lim_{h\to 0} \frac{1}{h}$\{output (per unit of time) at time t produced with capital produced in the time interval $(v, v + h)$\},

$L_v(t)$ = amount of labour working, at time t, with capital of vintage v, or, more precisely, $\lim_{h\to 0} \frac{1}{h}$\{amount of labour working at time t with capital produced in the time interval $(v, v + h)$\},

$I(t)$ = real gross investment (i.e. real expenditure per unit of time on new equipment) at time t,

$C(t)$ = real consumption at time t,

$Q(t)$ = gross output at time t,

$p(t)$ = price level at time t,

$w(t)$ = wage rate at time t,

$L(t)$ = total amount of labour employed at time t,

$L_s(t)$ = labour supply at time t,

B, b, s, ρ, δ = positive constants ($b > 1$, $s < 1$).

Equation (7.1.1) represents an infinite set of production functions, one for each vintage of capital. It implies that new technical knowledge is continually being embodied in new types of durable equipment (i.e. there is *embodied technical progress*), so that capital of a given vintage is more productive than that of any earlier vintage. And, since (7.1.1) holds for both $v < t$ and $v = t$, it implies that the ex-post and ex-ante elasticities of substitution are equal, each being -1.

Equation (7.1.2) assumes that the amount of capital of a given vintage decreases at a constant proportional rate, δ, per unit of time. This assumption can be interpreted in either of two ways. We can assume that each type of machine retains its original efficiency throughout its life, but that the number of machines of a given type that are still in existence decreases at a constant proportional rate. Or we can assume that the life of each machine is infinite, but that its efficiency decreases at a constant proportional rate.

Equation (7.1.3) assumes that real consumption is a constant proportion of gross output. This is not quite equivalent to assuming that consumption is a constant proportion of net income. For net income equals gross output minus depreciation. Depreciation is the decrease in the market value of capital resulting from both physical decay and obsolescence, the latter being a consequence of embodied technical progress. Hence, in order to introduce the assumption that consumption is a constant proportion of net income, it would be necessary to include in the model an equation determining the market value of capital and subtract the rate of change in the real market value of capital from $Q(t)$ in the consumption relation. For simplicity we avoid this by assuming the relation (7.1.3).

Equation (7.1.4) assumes that the amount of labour working with any vintage of capital is such that the marginal cost of the output obtained from that vintage of capital equals the price of a unit of output. This is the condition for profit maximisation under perfect competition. It implies that the total amount of labour employed is allocated between different vintages of capital in such a way that the marginal products of labour working with different vintages of capital are equal. Solow (1960) introduced the latter assumption directly. Here we have introduced prices in order to emphasise that, under perfect competition, the condition will be brought about by the price mechanism and does not require that each firm should use all vintages of capital.

Equations (7.1.5) and (7.1.6) follow directly from the definitions of the variables, (7.1.7) assumes that the labour supply grows at a constant proportional rate and (7.1.8) that output equals demand. Equation (7.1.9) assumes that the demand for labour equals the supply, or, in other words, that there is a continuous state of full employment. As in the models discussed in Chapter 4, we can regard this equation as a condition on investment.

The wage rate, w, is assumed to be exogenous. The paths of the remaining variables, including the infinite sets of variables $K_v(t)$, $L_v(t)$ and $Q_v(t)$ are determined by the model.

From (7.1.1), (7.1.2) and (7.1.4) we obtain

$$L_v(t) = B^{1/(1-b)}\left\{\frac{p(t)}{bw(t)}\right\}^{b/(b-1)} e^{\sigma v - \delta t} I(v), \tag{7.1.10}$$

$$Q_v(t) = B^{1/(1-b)}\left\{\frac{p(t)}{bw(t)}\right\}^{1/(b-1)} e^{\sigma v - \delta t} I(v), \tag{7.1.11}$$

where

$$\sigma = \delta + \frac{\rho}{b-1}.$$

And, from (7.1.5), (7.1.6), (7.1.10) and (7.1.11), we obtain

$$L(t) = B^{1/(1-b)}\left\{\frac{p(t)}{bw(t)}\right\}^{b/(b-1)} e^{-\delta t} \int_{-\infty}^{t} e^{\sigma v} I(v)\, dv, \tag{7.1.12}$$

$$Q(t) = B^{1/(1-b)}\left\{\frac{p(t)}{bw(t)}\right\}^{1/(b-1)} e^{-\delta t} \int_{-\infty}^{t} e^{\sigma v}\, I(v)\, dv, \tag{7.1.13}$$

which yield

$$L(t) = Be^{-\rho t}\{Q(t)\}^{b}\left\{\int_{-\infty}^{t} e^{-\sigma(t-v)}\, I(v)\, dv\right\}^{1-b} \tag{7.1.14}$$

Thus $L(t)$ is related to $Q(t)$, $\int_{-\infty}^{t} e^{-\sigma(t-v)}\, I(v)\, dv$ and t in the same way as it was assumed to be related to $Y(t)$, $K(t)$ and t in the models discussed in Chapters 4 to 6.

Under competitive conditions $\int_{-\infty}^{t} e^{-\sigma(t-v)}\, I(v)\, dv$ is the real market value of capital. For it is clear, from (7.1.1) and (7.1.2), that $e^{\rho(t-v)/(b-1)}$ units of capital of vintage v are, at all points of time from t onwards, a perfect substitute in production for a unit of capital of vintage t. But the real market value, at time t, of a unit of capital of vintage t must equal its real cost of production, unity. Hence the real market value, at time t, of a unit of capital of vintage v must be $e^{-\rho(t-v)/(b-1)}$. But the number of units of capital of vintages v to $v + dv$ in existence at time t is $e^{-\delta(t-v)}\, dv$. Hence the real market value, at time t, of the total amount of capital of all vintages is $\int_{-\infty}^{t} e^{-\sigma(t-v)}\, dv$.

From (7.1.7), (7.1.9) and (7.1.14) we obtain

$$DQ(t) = \frac{b-1}{b}\left\{\frac{L_0}{B}\right\}^{1/(b-1)} e^{(\rho+l)t/(b-1)} Q(t)^{1/(1-b)}\, I(t) + \frac{1}{b}\{l - \delta(b-1)\}\, Q(t), \tag{7.1.15}$$

which, together with (7.1.3) and (7.1.8) yields

$$(7.1.16) \quad DQ = \frac{s(b-1)}{b}\left\{\frac{L_0}{B}\right\}^{1/(b-1)} e^{(\rho+l)t/(b-1)} Q^{(b-2)/(b-1)} + \frac{1}{b}\{l - \delta(b-1)\}Q.$$

where $Q = Q(t)$. The solution of (7.1.16) is

$$(7.1.17) \quad Q = [\{Q^* e^{(\rho+l)t}\}^{1/(b-1)} + Ae^{\{l-(b-1)\delta\}t/b(b-1)}]^{b-1},$$

where

$$(7.1.18) \quad Q^* = \left\{\frac{(b-1)s}{b\rho + (b-1)(\delta + l)}\right\}^{b-1} \frac{L_0}{B},$$

and $\quad A = Q(0)^{1/(b-1)} - Q^{*1/(b-1)}.$

It is clear from (7.1.17) that the proportional deviation of Q from its equilibrium growth path, $Q^*e^{(\rho+l)t}$, tends to zero as $t \longrightarrow \infty$. It is interesting to compare $Q^*e^{(\rho+l)t}$ with the equilibrium growth path of output generated by the simple neo-classical model (see section 4.1). Let us assume, for this purpose, that $\delta = 0$, so that all equipment has an infinite life. (In Chapters 3 to 6 the complications associated with depreciation were avoided by defining Y as net output.) Then the only difference between the simple neo-classical model and the model under discussion is that in the former model technical progress has an equal effect on the productivity of all vintages of capital, whereas in the latter it affects the productivity of currently produced capital only. From (4.1.22) and (7.1.18) we obtain, assuming $\delta = 0$,

$$(7.1.19) \quad \frac{Y^*}{Q^*} = \left\{1 + \frac{\rho}{(b-1)(\rho + l)}\right\}^{b-1},$$

so that $Y^* > Q^*$, as we should expect.

Suppose, for example, that $\rho = 0{\cdot}04$, $l = 0{\cdot}01$ and $b = 1{\cdot}5$. Then $Y^*/Q^* = 1{\cdot}61$. But this should not be taken as an indication of the magnitude of the error of prediction that would be obtained by applying the simple neo-classical model to data generated by the model under discussion. For, if the parameters of (4.1.3) were estimated from data generated by the latter model, the estimated value of B would be less than its true value in (7.1.1).

7.2 Embodied Technical Progress with No Ex-Post Substitution

We now consider a model in which there is no ex-post substitution between labour and capital. The model which is due to Johansen (1959) is:

$$(7.2.1) \quad L_t(t) = Be^{-\rho t}Q_t(t)^b K_t(t)^{1-b} = Be^{-\rho t}Q_t(t)^b I(t)^{1-b},$$

$$\frac{Q_v(t)}{K_v(t)} = \frac{Q_v(v)}{K_v(v)} \qquad (v < t), \tag{7.2.2}$$

$$\frac{L_v(t)}{K_v(t)} = \frac{L_v(v)}{K_v(v)} \qquad (v < t), \tag{7.2.3}$$

$$K_v(t) = e^{-\delta(t-v)}I(v) \qquad (v \leq t), \tag{7.2.4}$$

$$C(t) = (1 - s)Q(t), \tag{7.2.5}$$

$$Q(t) = \int_{-\infty}^{t} Q_v(t)\, dv, \tag{7.2.6}$$

$$L(t) = \int_{-\infty}^{t} L_v(t)\, dv, \tag{7.2.7}$$

$$L_s(t) = L_0 e^{lt}, \tag{7.2.8}$$

$$Q(t) = C(t) + I(t), \tag{7.2.9}$$

$$L(t) = L_s(t), \tag{7.2.10}$$

where all variables are as defined in the previous section. Thus the only difference between this model and that discussed in the previous section is that (7.1.1) and (7.1.4) are replaced by (7.2.1) to (7.2.3).

It is assumed that the only possible substitution between labour and capital is that obtained by variations in the design of capital equipment. Hence the production function (7.2.1) relates only to capital of the current vintage. It is assumed, in equations (7.2.2) and (7.2.3), that the output of a unit of capital of any earlier vintage and the amount of labour required in order to operate it were fixed at the time of its construction.

From equations (7.2.2) to (7.2.4) we obtain

$$Q_v(t) = e^{-\delta(t-v)}Q_v(v), \tag{7.2.11}$$

$$L_v(t) = e^{-\delta(t-v)}L_v(v), \tag{7.2.12}$$

which, together with (7.2.6) and (7.2.7), yield

$$Q(t) = \int_{-\infty}^{t} e^{-\delta(t-v)}Q_v(v)\, dv, \tag{7.2.13}$$

$$L(t) = \int_{-\infty}^{t} e^{-\delta(t-v)}L_v(v)\, dv, \tag{7.2.14}$$

Differentiating (7.2.13) and (7.2.14) we obtain

$$DQ(t) = Q_t(t) - \delta Q(t), \tag{7.2.15}$$

$$DL(t) = L_t(t) - \delta L(t), \tag{7.2.16}$$

and, from (7.2.8), (7.2.10) and (7.2.16),

$$L_t(t) = L_0(l + \delta)e^{lt}. \tag{7.2.17}$$

From (7.2.1), (7.2.5), (7.2.9), (7.2.15) and (7.2.17) we obtain

$$(7.2.18)\quad DQ(t) = \left\{\frac{L_0(l+\delta)}{B}\right\}^{1/b}\{sQ(t)\}^{(b-1)/b}\, e^{(\rho+l)t/b} - \delta Q(t),$$

whose solution is

$$(7.2.19)\quad Q(t) = [\{Q^* e^{(\rho+l)t}\}^{1/b} + Ae^{-\delta t/b}]^b,$$

where

$$(7.2.20)\quad Q^* = \frac{L_0(l+\delta)s^{b-1}}{B(\rho+l+\delta)^b},$$

and

$$A = Q(0)^{1/b} - Q^{*1/b}.$$

It is clear, from (7.2.19), that the proportional deviation of Q from its equilibrium growth path, $Q^* e^{(\rho+l)t}$, tends to zero as $t \longrightarrow \infty$. Moreover, a comparison of (7.1.18) and (7.2.20) shows that the equilibrium growth path generated by Johansen's model is lower than that generated by Solow's model. For

$$\frac{(l+\delta)\{b\rho+(b-1)(\delta+l)\}^{b-1}}{(\rho+l+\delta)^b\,(b-1)^{b-1}}$$

$$= \left(1 - \frac{\rho}{\rho+l+\delta}\right)\left(1 + \frac{\rho}{(b-1)(\rho+l+\delta)}\right)^{b-1} < 1.$$

In view of the ex-post substitution allowed for in Solow's model this result is not surprising.

Although the technological assumptions of the above model are, perhaps, more realistic than those of any of the other models discussed so far, the behaviour assumptions are, in one respect, less realistic. For it is assumed, not only that there is a continuous state of full employment but also that all capital is used for the whole of its physical life. Even if the interest and real wage rates vary in such a way that the former condition is always satisfied, there is no reason (under Johansen's technological assumptions) for expecting an economy to converge to the state in which the latter condition is satisfied.

Suppose, for example, that, at time t, we have

$$(7.2.21)\quad \int_{-\infty}^{t} e^{-\delta(t-v)} L_v(v)\, dv > L_s(t)$$

which means that the total amount of labour required in order to operate all vintages of capital to full capacity exceeds the labour force.

Then, under competitive conditions with instantaneous adjustments of the wage rate, we must have

$$L_{t}'(t')w(t) = Q_{t}'(t')p(t), \tag{7.2.22}$$

where t' is determined by

$$\int_{t'}^{t} e^{-\delta(t-v)} L_v(v)\, dv = L_s(t). \tag{7.2.23}$$

Equations (7.2.22) and (7.2.23) imply that the real wage rate, $\frac{w(t)}{p(t)}$, will be determined in such a way that, if capital of vintages t' and later is just sufficient to absorb the labour force, capital of vintage t' earns a zero profit, capital of a later vintage than t' earns a positive profit and capital of an earlier vintage than t' can be operated only at a loss. Now, because of (7.2.5) and (7.2.9), we must have

$$I(t) = s\int_{t'}^{t} e^{-\delta(t-v)} Q_v(v)\, dv. \tag{7.2.24}$$

This can be regarded as a condition on the interest rate. The interest rate must be just low enough to induce entrepreneurs to invest enough to absorb the excess of full employment output over consumption. Thus the real wage rate and interest rate, at time t, are determined by the above conditions. Now the production function (7.2.1), the real wage rate, the interest rate and expectations about the future behaviour of these variables will determine the most profitable design of new equipment or, equivalently, the ratio $L_t(t)/I(t)$.

It is clear, therefore, that by introducing the interest and real wage rates, together with certain assumptions about the formation of cx-pectations concerning these variables, we can obtain a determinate system which does not generally converge to a state in which all capital is used for the whole of its physical life. Such a system was formulated by Phelps (1963), but is difficult to solve.

7.3 Endogenous Technical Progress

The models discussed in the preceding sections retain the classical assumption that the acquisition of technical knowledge depends only on the passage of time. For they assume that the number of units of labour required in order to produce any given output with a unit of capital of the current vintage is a decreasing exponential function of time. Thus technical progress is treated as exogenous. It is generally recognised, however, that this method of allowing for technical progress is a confession of ignorance and that there is scope for the formulation of more realistic hypotheses which allow for the influence of the economic environment on the rate of acquisition of knowledge.

One such hypothesis has been formulated by Arrow (1962). His broad hypothesis is that the stimulus to "learning" (the acquisition of technical knowledge) is provided by the construction of new types of capital equipment, so that the efficiency of the most recent vintage of capital depends on cumulative gross investment. (A more complicated hypothesis in which gross investment is the basic agent of technical charge was used by Kaldor and Mirrlees (1962).) In order to formulate Arrow's hypothesis more precisely it is necessary to distinguish different vintages of capital by the levels of cumulative gross investment at the times when they were produced and not by their dates of construction as in the models of Solow and Johansen. Capital produced at the time when cumulative gross investment reached G will be said to have serial number G. It is assumed, for simplicity, that all technical progress is embodied and that there is no substitution, either ex-ante or ex-post, between labour and capital. The hypothesis can then be formulated in terms of two functions $\lambda(G)$ and $\gamma(G)$ where:

$\gamma(G)$ = output capacity of a unit of capital with serial number G,
$\lambda(G)$ = amount of labour required in order to produce $\gamma(G)$ units of output with a unit of capital with serial number G.

We assume that $\gamma(G)$ is a non-decreasing function and $\lambda(G)$ a non-increasing function. Then, under competitive conditions, capital with a given serial number will not be used unless every unit of capital with a higher serial number is used to full capacity. And, assuming that the physical life of capital exceeds its economic life, we have

$$Q = \int_{G'}^{G} \gamma(G)\, dG, \tag{7.3.1}$$

$$L = \int_{G'}^{G} \lambda(G)\, dG, \tag{7.3.2}$$

where
Q = total output,
L = total amount of labour employed,
G = cumulative gross investment,
G' = serial number of oldest capital in use.

The magnitudes Q, L, G and G' are, of course, all functions of time.

Now let $\Gamma(G)$ and $\Lambda(G)$ be defined by

$$\Gamma(G) = \int \gamma(G)\, dG, \tag{7.3.3}$$

$$\Lambda(G) = \int \lambda(G)\, dG, \tag{7.3.4}$$

Then (7.3.1) and (7.3.2) can be written

$$Q = \Gamma(G) - \Gamma(G'), \tag{7.3.5}$$

(7.3.6) $$L = \Lambda(G) - \Lambda(G').$$

Eliminating G' from (7.3.5) and (7.3.6) we obtain

(7.3.7) $$Q = \Gamma(G) - \Gamma[\Lambda^{-1}\{\Lambda(G) - L\}],$$

which is a rather novel form of production function.

Consider now the interpretation of the derivative of this function with respect to L. Let δQ and $\delta G'$ denote the increments in Q and G' resulting from a small increment, δL, in L, when G is constant. Then

(7.3.8) $$\frac{\partial Q}{\partial L} = \lim_{\delta L \to 0} \frac{\delta Q}{\delta L} = \lim_{\delta L \to 0} \left\{ \frac{\delta Q}{\delta G'} \Big/ \frac{\delta L}{\delta G'} \right\} = \frac{\gamma(G')}{\lambda(G')}.$$

Hence $\frac{\partial Q}{\partial L}$ is the output of a unit of labour working with capital of serial number G' (i.e. the least efficient capital in use).

Now, assuming perfect competition, we must have

(7.3.9) $$w\lambda(G') = p\gamma(G'),$$

where w and p denote the wage rate and price level respectively. For if $w\lambda(G'') > p\gamma(G'')$ capital with serial number G'' will be left unused, while if $w\lambda(G'') < p\gamma(G'')$ some capital with a lower serial number than G'' will be used. It follows from (7.3.8) and (7.3.9) that, under perfect competition, we have the usual condition

(7.3.10) $$\frac{\partial Q}{\partial L} = \frac{w}{p},$$

or $$p = w\frac{\partial L}{\partial Q}.$$

Arrow (1962) constructed a complete model assuming that

(7.3.11) $$\gamma(G) = a,$$

(7.3.12) $$\lambda(G) = bG^{-n},$$

where $a > 0$, $b > 0$ and $1 > n > 0$. He assumed also that there is perfect competition and a continuous state of full employment and that the ratio of consumption to total output is a function of the rate of interest. Here we consider the special case in which the ratio of consumption to output is constant. The model is then

(7.3.13) $$Q = aG\left[1 - \left\{1 - \frac{(1-n)L}{bG^{1-n}}\right\}^{1/(1-n)}\right],$$

(7.3.14) $$C = (1 - s)Q,$$

(7.3.15) $$L_s = L_0 e^{lt},$$

(7.3.16) $$Q = C + DG,$$

.3.17) $$L = L_s,$$

where the variables other than G are as defined in the previous sections. Equation (7.3.13) is obtained from (7.3.3), (7.3.4), (7.3.7), (7.3.11) and (7.3.12).

Eliminating Q, C, L and L_s from the above system we obtain

(7.3.18) $$DG = saG\left[1 - \left\{1 - \frac{(1-n)L_0 e^{lt}}{bG^{1-n}}\right\}^{1/(1-n)}\right],$$

which has a particular solution

(7.3.19) $$G = G^* e^{lt/(1-n)},$$

where

(7.3.20) $$G^* = \frac{\left\{\frac{(1-n)L_0}{b}\right\}^{1/(1-n)}}{\left[1 - \left\{1 - \frac{l}{as(1-n)}\right\}^{1-n}\right]^{1/(1-n)}}.$$

From (7.3.13), (7.3.19) and (7.3.20) we obtain the equilibrium growth path of output,

(7.3.21) $$Q = Q^* e^{lt/(1-n)}$$

where

(7.3.22) $$Q^* = \frac{\left\{\frac{(1-n)L_0}{b}\right\}^{1/(1-n)}}{\left[\left\{\frac{s(1-n)}{l}\right\}^{1-n} - \left\{\frac{s(1-n)}{l} - \frac{1}{a}\right\}^{1-n}\right]^{1/(1-n)}}.$$

We note that the equilibrium growth rate of output is independent of s and an increasing function of l, but that $\frac{\partial Q^*}{\partial s} > 0$ and $\frac{\partial Q^*}{\partial l} < 0$. These implications of the model are shared by all of the growth models previously discussed. But an implication not shared by the previous models is that the equilibrium growth rate of output per unit of labour is proportional to l. All of the previous growth models imply that the equilibrium growth rate of output per unit of labour equals ρ, while Arrow's model implies that it equals $\frac{nl}{(1-n)}$.

It is clear from (7.3.22) that a necessary condition for the existence of an equilibrium growth path (with full employment) is that $s \geq \frac{l}{a(1-n)}$. This is a consequence of the assumption that there is no substitution, either ex ante or ex post, between labour and capital. For, if there is no substitution between labour and capital and s is too small, a stage will be reached when there is insufficient capital to keep the labour force fully employed.

Let us assume now that $s > \frac{l}{a(1-n)}$, and consider the stability of the system. From equations (7.3.18) and (7.3.20) we obtain

$$(7.3.23)\quad Dg = sa - \frac{l}{1-n} - \left[\left(sa - \frac{l}{1-n}\right)^{1-n} + \left\{(sa)^{1-n} - \left(sa - \frac{l}{1-n}\right)^{1-n}\right\}(1 - e^{-(1-n)g})\right]^{1/(1-n)},$$

where $\quad g = \log \{G/G^* e^{lt/(1-n)}\}$.

Hence Dg is a continuous decreasing function of g which is defined for all g and equal to zero when $g = 0$. It follows that, whatever the initial value of g, we have $\lim_{t\to\infty} g = 0$, so that the proportion deviations of G and Q from their equilibrium growth paths tend to zero as $t \longrightarrow \infty$.

7.4 A Reconsideration of the Production Function

Each of the alternative technological assumptions discussed so far is, in some sense, more realistic than the others. Hence our ultimate aim should be to construct a model that incorporates some sort of synthesis of these assumptions. Such a model should allow for the following features of reality:

(1) Although most technical progress is of the embodied sort, there is some progress that affects the productivity of labour working with existing capital.

(2) There is both ex-ante and ex-post substitution between labour and capital, but the degree of ex-ante substitution exceeds the degree of ex-post substitution.

(3) Since "learning" takes time the productivity of the current vintage of capital depends not only on cumulative gross investment, G, but also on the distribution of G over time.

If the model is to be used for prediction and regulation it should also explain fluctuations in the level of employment and be amenable to mathematical and statistical analysis. In view of the difficulty of constructing such a model, some consideration should be given to the predictive power of a model incorporating a production function of the form (4.1.1) when applied to data generated by a system of the above sort. Let us start by considering a system in which all technical progress is embodied and there is no substitution, either ex ante or ex post, between labour and capital These are the conditions under which the predictive power of a model incorporating a production function of the form (4.1.1) would seem to be weakest. Our basic technical assumptions are as follows:

(1) The output capacity of a unit of capital of any vintage is a constant, a.

(2) The amount of labour required in order to produce a units of output with a unit of capital of the current vintage decreases at a constant proportional rate, ρ per unit of time. Thus $be^{-\rho t}$ units of labour are required in order to produce a units of output with a unit of capital of the current vintage.

(3) The amount of capital of a given vintage decreases at a constant proportional rate, δ per unit of time.

(4) Capital of a given vintage is not used unless all capital of a later vintage is used to full capacity.

From these assumptions we obtain

$$K = \int_{-\infty}^{t} I(v)e^{-\delta(t-v)}\, dv, \tag{7.4.1}$$

$$Q = a\int_{t-q}^{t} I(v)e^{-\delta(t-v)}\, dv, \tag{7.4.2}$$

$$L = b\int_{t-q}^{t} I(v)e^{-\delta(t-v)-\rho v}\, dv, \tag{7.4.3}$$

where K = total amount of capital in existence,
I = gross investment,
Q = gross output,
L = amount of labour employed,
q = age of oldest vintage of capital in use.

Suppose now that the relations (7.4.1) to (7.4.3) are incorporated in a complete cyclical growth model. In such a model q will oscillate with the same frequency as output and employment. Moreover, at certain stages of the cycle, we may have $Dq > 1$, in which case capital that became idle during the preceding recession will be brought back into use. In order to allow for this possibility we have assumed, for simplicity, that capital is never scrapped but that its rate of physical decay is the same when it is idle as when it is being used. These assumptions are implicit in (7.4.1).

Let us confine our attention to models that have a particular solution in which Q and K each grow at the constant proportional rate σ, while L grows at the constant proportional rate l. Then we must have $\sigma = \rho + l$. For, differentiating (7.4.1) and substituting

$$K = K^* e^{\sigma t} \tag{7.4.4}$$

we obtain

$$I = (\sigma + \delta)K^* e^{\sigma t} \tag{7.4.5}$$

which, together with (7.4.2) and

$$Q = Q^* e^{\sigma t}, \tag{7.4.6}$$

yields

$$q = -\frac{1}{\sigma + \delta} \log \left(1 - \frac{Q^*}{aK^*}\right). \tag{7.4.7}$$

Thus, when Q and K are on their equilibrium growth paths, q is constant. Now, from (7.4.3) and (7.4.5), we obtain

$$L = \frac{b(\sigma + \delta)K^*}{\sigma + \delta - \rho}(1 - e^{-(\sigma+\delta-\rho)q})e^{(\sigma-\rho)t}. \tag{7.4.8}$$

Hence, if L is growing at the constant proportional rate l, we must have $\sigma = \rho + l$.

Consider now a situation in which K is always on its equilibrium growth path (i.e. $K = K^* e^{(\rho+l)t}$ for all t), while Q oscillates in an arbitrary manner. This sort of behaviour of Q and K could not, of course, be generated by a realistic model. But, as a first step, let us consider how L would behave if Q and K did behave in this way. From (7.4.2), (7.4.4) and (7.4.5) we obtain

$$Q = aK(1 - e^{-(\rho+l+\delta)q}), \tag{7.4.9}$$

and, from (7.4.3), (7.4.4) and (7.4.5),

$$L = \frac{b(\rho + l + \delta)}{l + \delta}(1 - e^{-(l+\delta)q})e^{-\rho t}K. \tag{7.4.10}$$

Eliminating q from (7.4.9) and (7.4.10) we obtain

$$L = \frac{b(\rho + l + \delta)}{l + \delta}e^{-\rho t}K\left[1 - \left\{1 - \frac{Q}{aK}\right\}^{(l+\delta)/(\rho+l+\delta)}\right], \tag{7.4.11}$$

or

$$Q = aK\left[1 - \left\{1 - \frac{(l + \delta)e^{\rho t}L}{b(\rho + l + \delta)K}\right\}^{(\rho+l+\delta)/(l+\delta)}\right]. \tag{7.4.12}$$

This relation has the properties of a production function which shows constant returns to scale and has a diminishing marginal rate of substitution between factors. Moreoever, by an argument similar to that used in the preceding section, we see that $\frac{\partial Q}{\partial L}$ is the output of a unit of labour working with the least efficient capital in use. Hence, under perfect competition, we have (7.3.10). We note, incidentally, that there is an interesting similarity between (7.3.13) and (7.4.12) which were obtained, independently, by Arrow (1962) and Bergstrom (1962) respectively.

The reason why the relation (7.4.11) is satisfied if K is always on its equilibrium growth path is that the age distribution of capital is then constant. But, in a realistic model, any deviation of Q from its equilibrium growth path causes a deviation of K from its equilibrium growth path. Nevertheless, provided that the proportional deviations are small, the age distribution of capital does not change much and (7.4.11) is approximately satisfied (see Bergstrom (1962)). Hence a model incorporating (7.4.11) instead of the assumed true relations (7.1.2) and (7.1.3) can be expected to yield good predictions provided that the system remains sufficiently close to the steady state. (See Bergstrom (1962) for a complete cyclical growth model incorporating this sort of production function.)

It must be remembered, however, that (7.4.11) was (like Arrow's relation (7.3.13)) derived from the rather unrealistic assumption that there is no substitution, either ex ante or ex post, between capital of a particular vintage and labour. If ex-ante substitution is possible, then a model incorporating a more convenient production function such as the Cobb–Douglas function might predict equally well. An interesting simulation study by Solow (1963) provides some support for this conjecture.

CHAPTER 8

MULTI-SECTOR MODELS

ALL of the models discussed in the preceding five chapters, except the two-sector neo-classical model (see section 4.2), are single sector models of an economy. That is to say, they are formally equivalent to models of an economy that produces only a single good which can be either consumed or transformed, at no cost, into fixed capital. There is considerable scope for further development of the two-sector model by relaxing the assumption of full employment and introducing monetary phenomena, as in Chapter 5, and by introducing more realistic assumptions concerning technical progress as in Chapter 7. But our ultimate aim should be to construct realistic multi-sector models. For such models can take account of the interactions between a large number of different sectors of the economy, and hence, provided that their parameters can be estimated with sufficient accuracy, should yield more accurate predictions than the simpler models.

Several important general problems arise in connection with the construction and use of such models. The first arises from the fact that, if all *a priori* information is ignored, the number of parameters will be of the order n^2, while the amount of data available for estimation purposes will be of the order n, where n is the number of variables. Hence, in order to ensure that there is a sufficient number of degrees of freedom in the sample, it is necessary to rely heavily on economic theory and other sources of *a priori* information. We then have the important problem of how to make the most efficient use of this information. A closely associated problem is that of finding simple conditions governing the behaviour of the model. This is particularly important when the parameters are subject to severe *a priori* restrictions. It is important that we should know the conditions under which a model incorporating these restrictions displays certain features of reality. Finally, we have the problem of choosing particular functional forms that are good approximations to reality and are such that, when the various relations are fitted together, the complete model is amenable to mathematical and statistical analysis.

Research on the above problems is still in the early stages, and the multi-sector models whose properties have been studied intensively are, apart from the multiplicity of sectors, simpler and less realistic than most of the models discussed in the previous chapters. We shall confine the discussion to two basic models, one of which is essentially due to the nineteenth century economist, Walras (1954), and the other to Leontief (1953).

8.1 The Walrasian Model

We shall consider an economy with l individuals, m variable factors of production (say various types of labour) and n products. The Walrasian model is then:

(8.1.1) $$L^s_{ik} = L^s_{ik}(w_1, \ldots, w_m, p_1, \ldots, p_n) \qquad (i = 1, \ldots, m) \quad (k = 1, \ldots, l),$$

(8.1.2) $$C_{jk} = C_{jk}(w_1, \ldots, w_m, p_1, \ldots, p_n) \qquad (j = 1, \ldots, n) \quad (k = 1, \ldots, l),$$

(8.1.3) $$L_i = \sum_{j=1}^{n} a_{ij}C_j \qquad (i = 1, \ldots, m),$$

(8.1.4) $$L^s_i = \sum_{k=1}^{l} L^s_{ik} \qquad (i = 1, \ldots, m),$$

(8.1.5) $$C_j = \sum_{k=1}^{l} C_{jk} \qquad (j = 1, \ldots, n),$$

(8.1.6) $$p_j = \sum_{i=1}^{m} a_{ij}w_i \qquad (j = 1, \ldots, n),$$

(8.1.7) $$Dw_i = \beta_i(L_i - L^s_i) \qquad (i = 1, \ldots, m),$$

where L^s_{ik} = supply of factor i by individual k,
L^s_i = total supply of factor i,
L_i = total demand for factor i,
C_{jk} = demand for product j by individual k,
C_j = total demand for product j,
p_j = price of product j,
w_i = price of factor i,
a_{ij}, β_i = non-negative constants.

We assume that the functions $L^s_{1k}, \ldots, L^s_{mk}, C_{1k}, \ldots, C_{nk}$ are such that, for any set of values of the w_i's and p_j's, $U_k\{L^s_{1k}(w_1, \ldots, p_n), \ldots, C_{nk}(w_1, \ldots, p_n)\}$ is the maximum of a utility function $U_k\{L^s_{1k}, \ldots, L^s_{mk}, C_{1k}, \ldots, C_{nk}\}$ subject to the *budget constraint*,

(8.1.8) $$\sum_{j=1}^{n} p_jC_{jk} = \sum_{i=1}^{m} w_iL^s_{ik}$$

where the function U_k is defined on the set of vectors, of dimension $m + n$, whose elements are non-negative. The equations (8.1.1) and (8.1.2) then imply that, at any given set of prices of the factors and products, each individual plans to sell certain quantities of the various factors and buy certain quantities of the various products, the quantities chosen by any individual being such as to maximise his satisfaction or utility subject to the condition that his planned expenditure equals his planned receipts. Assuming that the utility functions are differentiable, the necessary conditions for the maximisation of the utility of individual k are

$$\frac{\partial}{\partial C_{jk}} U_k(L^s_{1k}, \ldots, C_{nk}) = \mu p_j \qquad (j = 1, \ldots, n), \tag{8.1.9}$$

$$\frac{\partial}{\partial L^s_{ik}} U_k(L^s_{1k}, \ldots, C_{nk}) = -\mu w_i \qquad (i = 1, \ldots, m), \tag{8.1.10}$$

where μ is a Lagrange multiplier. The solution of the system of equations (8.1.8) to (8.1.10) for each k yields the system of supply and demand equations (8.1.1) and (8.1.2). We implicitly assume that the utility functions are such that the equations (8.1.8) to (8.1.10) have a unique solution and that the sufficient conditions for a maximum are satisfied.

It should be noted that, if, in (8.1.9) and (8.1.10), we replace U_k by $\phi(U_k)$ where ϕ is any function for which $\phi'(x) > 0$, the solution of (8.1.8) to (8.1.10) is unaffected. Hence the above theory does not imply that utility is measurable.

The a_{ij}'s can be interpreted as technological coefficients. Thus a_{ij} is the number of units of factor i used in the production of one unit of product j. The assumption that these coefficients are constants is made for simplicity, but is unrealistic to the extent that it makes no allowance for substitution between factors in response to changes in their relative prices. In a more realistic version of the model the a_{ij}'s are assumed to be functions of factor prices obtained by minimising the unit cost of production subject to the constraints of a production function.

The equations (8.1.6) assume that the price of each product equals its unit cost of production. Thus we implicitly assume a state of perfect competition. Equations (8.1.7) assume that the rate of increase in the price of each factor is proportional to the excess demand for it. Walras did not specify a precise form of price adjustment equation, but, in a non-mathematical explanation of how the system would reach equilibrium, assumed that when the demand for any factor exceeds the supply, the price will rise, and when the supply exceeds the demand the price will fall. The first rigorous study of the dynamic properties of a Walrasian system is due to Samuelson (1941).

Substituting from (8.1.1) and (8.1.2) into (8.1.4) and (8.1.5) we obtain

$$L^s_i = L^s_i(w_1, \ldots, w_m, p_1, \ldots, p_n) \qquad (i = 1, \ldots, m), \tag{8.1.11}$$

$$C_j = C_j(w_1, \ldots, w_m, p_1, \ldots, p_n) \qquad (j = 1, \ldots, n). \tag{8.1.12}$$

We now have a model, comprising equations (8.1.3), (8.1.6), (8.1.7), (8.1.11) and (8.1.12), which involves only the L^s_i's, L_i's, C_j's, w_i's and p_j's. It is with this model that we are directly concerned in econometric applications. For our ultimate aim is to explain and predict the market variables rather than the variables relating to individuals. Nevertheless, the assumption that the model involving market variables only is derived from the more basic model comprising equations (8.1.1) to (8.1.7), and that the functions L^s_{ik} and C_{jk} are obtained from the maximisation of a utility function subject to the budget constraint, is important. For it provides us with a source of *a priori* restrictions on the system of equations (8.1.11) and (8.1.12).

The most obvious restriction is that the equation

$$(8.1.13) \qquad \sum_{j=1}^{n} p_j C_j = \sum_{i=1}^{m} w_i L^s_i$$

must be satisfied. This relation is known as the Walras law and is obtained by summing the equations (8.1.8) over $k = 1, \ldots l$. Another obvious restriction is that the functions $L^s_1, \ldots, L^s_m, C_1, \ldots, C_n$ must be homogeneous of the degree zero. For it is clear that an equal proportional increase in all the w_i's and p_j's does not affect the budget constraint, (8.1.8), and hence does not affect the values of the L^s_{ik}'s and C_{jk}'s that maximise a utility function subject to this constraint. But the above two restrictions are rather weak, and, unless the number of sectors is small relative to the number of observations of each variable, will not ensure that there are enough degrees of freedom in the sample to provide reliable estimates of the parameters of (8.1.11) and (8.1.12).

One way of obtaining stronger restrictions is to assume that the functions $L^s_1, \ldots, L^s_m, C_1, \ldots, C_n$ have the properties that they would necessarily have if the utility functions of all individuals in the economy were identical. More precisely, we assume that the functions $L^s_1, \ldots,$ $L^s m, C_1, \ldots, C_n$ are such that, for any set of non-negative values of the w_i's and p_j's, $U\{L^s_1, (w_1, \ldots, p_n), \ldots, C_n(w_1, \ldots, pn)\}$ is the maximum of a function $U\{L^s_1, \ldots, L^s_m, C_1, \ldots, C_n\}$ subject to the budget constraint (8.1.13). The existence of a function U, which is related to the market supply and demand functions in this way does not necessarily imply that the utility functions of different individuals are identical (or can be made identical by suitable monotonic transformations.) But it does place rather severe restrictions on the forms of these functions (see Gorman (1953)).

In econometric applications we can start by assuming a particular form of function, U, involving a number (of the order $m + n$) of unknown parameters. Then, by maximising U subject to (8.1.13), we obtain the forms of the functions $L^s_1, \ldots, L^s_m, C_1, \ldots, C_n$. (An equivalent procedure was used by Stone (1954*b*).) The number of unknown parameters in the $m + n$ equations (8.1.11) and (8.1.12) then equals the number of unknown parameters in U. The assumed form of U should be such that, for any set of non-negative values of the w_i's and p_j's, the constrained maximum exists and is continuous with respect to the w_i's and p_j's. And it should be such that the complete model, comprising equations (8.1.3), (8.1.6), (8.1.7), (8.1.11) and (8.1.12) has a particular solution: $L^*_1 = L^{s*}_1, \ldots, L^*_m = L^{s*}_m, C^*_1, \ldots, C^*_n,$

$w_1^*, \ldots, w_m^*, p_1^*, \ldots, p_n^*$, where all of these quantities are positive constants. Since the functions $L^s_1, \ldots, L^s_m, C_1, \ldots, C_n$ are homogeneous of degree zero in the prices of the factors and products, $L^*_1, \ldots, L^*_m, C^*_1, \ldots, C^*_n, \lambda w_1^*, \ldots, \lambda w^*_m, \lambda p_1^*, \ldots, \lambda p_n^*$, where λ is any positive constant, must also be a solution.

In the literature on the existence of competitive equilibrium (see, for example, Wald (1951) and Arrow and Debreu (1954)) the equilibrium values of some variables are allowed to be zero. Moreover, the equilibrium cost of a product is allowed to exceed its equilibrium price if its equilibrium output is zero, and the equilibrium supply of a factor is allowed to exceed its equilibrium demand if its equilibrium price is zero. It is argued that, if the model is realistic, it should be capable of explaining which potential products are produced, which factors are used and which products and factors are not free. But, in econometric applications, we are concerned only with products and factors that have been observed to come within these categories over a certain period. Hence the equilibrium values of the variables in a realistic econometric model should be positive.

Let us suppose, now, that the system of equations (8.1.11) and (8.1.12) are restricted in the above way and consider the dynamic behaviour of the complete model. We assume that the function U, from which (8.1.11) and (8.1.12) are derived is differentiable, has negative partial derivatives with respect to the L^s_i's and is such that the functions $L^s_1, \ldots, L^s_m, C_1, \ldots, C_n$ satisfy the Lipschitz condition (see Struble (1962)). Then, for any set of non-negative initial values of the w_i's, a solution of the system exists and is continuous with respect to the initial values. The assumption that $\partial U/\partial L^s_i < 0$ $(i = 1, \ldots, m)$ ensures that if at any time we have $w_i = 0$, then we must also have $L^s_i = 0$ and hence $Dw_i \geq 0$. We assume also that $\beta_i = 1 (i = 1, \ldots, m)$ so that (8.1.7) is replaced by

$$Dw_i = L_i - L^s_i. \tag{8.1.14}$$

Since, in the following argument, we shall use only those properties of the model that are independent of units of measurement, the last assumption involves no loss of generality. The column vectors $\{L^s_1, \ldots, L^s_m\}, \{L_1, \ldots, L_m\}, \{C_1, \ldots, C_n\}, \{w_1, \ldots, w_m\}$ and $\{p_1, \ldots, p_n\}$ will be represented by L^s, L, C, w and p, respectively, and the matrix of technological coefficients by A.

We consider first the behaviour of $w'w$. Using (8.1.14), (8.1.3), (8.1.6) and (8.1.13), successively, we obtain

$$\begin{aligned} D(w'w) &= 2w'(L - L^s) \\ &= 2w'(AC - L^s) \\ &= 2\{(w'A)C - w'L^s\} \\ &= 2(p'C - w'L^s) \\ &= 0. \end{aligned} \tag{8.1.15}$$

Hence we have

$$w'w = w(0)'w(0). \tag{8.1.16}$$

The geometrical interpretation of this result is that w remains on the surface of the hypersphere whose centre is the origin and radius is the Euclidean distance of the initial point $w(0)$ from the origin.

Now we know that, if $L^* = L^{s*}, C^*, w^*, p^*$ is a stationary solution of the system, then $L^*, C^*, \lambda w^*, \lambda p^*$, where λ is any positive scalar, is also a stationary solution. We have, in particular, a stationary solution L^*, C^*, w^{**}, p^{**} such that $w^{**\prime}w^{**} = w'(0)w(0)$. We shall now consider the behaviour of $V = (w - w^{**})'(w - w^{**})$ which is the squared Euclidean distance of w from the equilibrium point, w^{**}. Using (8.1.14) (8.1.3), (8.1.6) and (8.1.13), successively, we obtain

$$\begin{aligned} DV &= 2(w - w^{**})'(L - L^s) \\ &= 2\{w'L - w'L^s - w^{**\prime}(L - L^s)\} \\ &= 2\{w'AC - w'L^s - w^{**\prime}(L - L^s)\} \\ &= 2\{p'C - w'L^s - w^{**\prime}(L - L^s)\} \\ &= -2w^{**\prime}(L - L^s). \end{aligned} \tag{8.1.17}$$

Now let $\hat{w}$ and $\hat{p}$ be any vectors satisfying: $\hat{w} \geq 0, \hat{p} \geq 0, \hat{p}' = \hat{w}'A$, $\hat{w}'\hat{w} = w(0)'w(0)$, $\hat{w} \neq w^{**}$, and let $\hat{L}^s$ denote the column vector $\{L^s_1(\hat{w}', \hat{p}'), \ldots, L^s_m(\hat{w}', \hat{p}')\}$, and $\hat{C}$ the column vector $\{C_1(\hat{w}', \hat{p}'), \ldots, C_n(\hat{w}', \hat{p}')\}$. Then we have

$$\begin{aligned} \hat{p}'C^* - \hat{w}'L^{s*} &= \hat{w}'AC^* - \hat{w}'L^{s*} \\ &= \hat{w}'L^* - \hat{w}'L^{s*} \\ &= 0. \end{aligned} \tag{8.1.18}$$

But $U(\hat{L}^{s\prime}, \hat{C}')$ is the maximum of $U(L^{s\prime}, C')$ subject to the constraint $\hat{p}'C = \hat{w}'L^s$. Moreover, since $\hat{w} \neq w^{**}$ and $\hat{w}'\hat{w} = w^{**\prime}w^{**}$, while U is differentiable, we have $(\hat{L}^{s\prime}, \hat{C}') \neq (L^{s*\prime}, C^{*\prime})$. Hence, because of (8.1.18), we have

$$U(\hat{L}^{s\prime}, \hat{C}') > U(L^{s*\prime}, C^{*\prime}). \tag{8.1.19}$$

Now let $\hat{\hat{L}}^s$ and $\hat{\hat{C}}$ be any vectors satisfying: $\hat{\hat{L}}^s \geq 0$, $\hat{\hat{C}} \geq 0$, $p^{**\prime}\hat{\hat{C}} \leq w^{**\prime}\hat{\hat{L}}^s$. Then, since $\partial U/\partial L^s_i < 0 (i = 1, \ldots, m)$ and $U(L^{s*\prime}, C^{*\prime})$ is the maximum of $U(L^{s\prime}, C')$ subject to the constraint $p^{**\prime}C = w^{**\prime}L^s$, we have

$$U(L^{s*\prime}, C^{*\prime}) \geq U(\hat{\hat{L}}^{s\prime}, \hat{\hat{C}}'). \tag{8.1.20}$$

It follows that

$$p^{**\prime}\hat{C} > w^{**\prime}\hat{L}^s. \tag{8.1.21}$$

For otherwise we could put $\hat{\hat{L}}^s = \hat{L}^s$ and $\hat{\hat{C}} = \hat{C}$ in (8.1.20) and contradict (8.1.19). From (8.1.21) we obtain

$$w^{**'}(\hat{L} - \hat{L}^s) > 0, \tag{8.1.22}$$

where $\hat{L} = A\hat{C}$.

It follows from (8.1.17) and (8.1.22) that $DV < 0$ unless $w = w^{**}$. Hence, since $V \geq 0$, we have $\lim_{t\to\infty} V = V^{**} \geq 0$. We shall show, finally, that $V^{**} = 0$. Suppose that $V^{**} > 0$. Then, since DV is a continuous function of w and is negative unless $w = w^{**}$, it has a negative maximum, $-\sigma$, over the closed, bounded set of w's such that $V^{**} \leq V \leq V^{**} + \epsilon$ and $w'w = w(0)'w(0)$. Hence, for a sufficiently large t, we have $DV \leq -\sigma$ which implies that $V \longrightarrow -\infty$ as $t \longrightarrow \infty$, contradicting $V^{**} > 0$. Hence $V^{**} = 0$, so that we have

$$\lim_{t\to\infty} w = w^{**}. \tag{8.1.23}$$

This result shows not only that the system converges to a steady state, whatever the initial values of the variables, but also that the equilibrium price ratios and quantities supplied and demanded are unique. The above argument is an extension of that of Arrow, Block and Hurwicz (1959) (see also Morishima (1960).

We shall conclude this section with some brief comments on the realism of the above model and on possible extensions of it. In much of the literature, including Walras (1954), models of this sort are regarded as descriptions of a *tâtonnement process*. In such a process no products or factors are exchanged until the system reaches a state of equilibrium. Quantities supplied and demanded are merely offers which are adjusted continuously as prices change in response to excess demands. Thus the model is regarded as a description of the process by which the system approaches equilibrium and during which there are no transactions. But, if this were the only purpose of the model, it would hardly deserve the amount of attention that it has received. For most markets are not organised in this way.

Here we give a different interpretation of the model. Our main interest is in its potentiality as an econometric model. For this purpose it is essential that the variables should be observable. Hence we identify C_j with the quantity of product j sold (per unit of time) and L_i with the amount of factor i employed. An observable quantity to be identified with $L^s{}_i$ is more difficult to find. For equations (8.1.3), (8.1.6) and (8.1.13) imply that

$$w'L = w'L^s. \tag{8.1.24}$$

One possibility is to add to each L_i the recorded unemployment of the factor and then make equal proportional adjustments of the resulting quantities so that (8.1.24) is satisfied. This means, of course, that the model cannot explain variations in the general level of employment. Indeed, if there were only one factor of production, (8.1.24) would imply $L — L^s$.

The most obvious unrealistic feature of the model is that it makes no allowance for saving and investment. We could identify some of the C_i's with investment in various types of fixed capital. But the integrals of these variables should then have some influence on the a_{ij}'s. The a_{ij}'s should depend not only on the relative factor prices, as we have already observed, but also on the ratios of the outputs of the various products to the amounts of the various types of capital used in their production. In view of these complications, the most convenient way of introducing capital into the model is, perhaps, to replace (8.1.3) by a system of production functions in which the output of each product is assumed to be a function of the amounts of the various types of labour and various types of capital used in its production. Demand equations for the various types of labour could then be derived from the production functions and the assumption of profit maximisation, while (8.1.6) could be replaced by equations relating the price of each good to its marginal cost, which would be derived from the production function.

Another way in which the model could be made more realistic is by distinguishing between the output and sales of each product, thus allowing for the possibility of variations in stocks. The sales variables would occur in the demand equations and the output variables in the production functions. It would then be necessary to introduce some sort of output adjustment equations. We could assume, for example, that the rate of change in the output of each product is a function of the excess of sales over output and the excess of the desired stock over the actual stock.

Finally, the model could be extended to allow for the fact that many products are used, as current inputs, in the production of other products and, either directly or indirectly, in their own production. A special feature of the Leontief model, which will be discussed in the following section, is that it allows for this type of interdependence.

8.2 The Leontief Model

We shall consider an economy with n sectors and n goods. We assume that each sector has a single output which is the total supply of one of the goods, has a current input of at least one good, and holds a stock of at least one good. We shall regard sector n as the household sector and good n as labour. The Leontief model is then:

(8.2.1) $$Q_{ij} = a_{ij}Q_j \qquad (i = 1, \ldots, n), \; (j = 1, \ldots, n),$$

(8.2.2) $$S_{ij} = b_{ij}Q_j \qquad (i = 1, \ldots, n) \; (j = 1, \ldots, n),$$

$$Q_i = \sum_{j=1}^{n} Q_{ij} + \sum_{j=1}^{n} DS_{ij} \qquad (i = 1, \ldots, n), \tag{8.2.3}$$

where $Q_j =$ output of good j,
$Q_{ij} =$ current input of good i by sector j,
$S_{ij} =$ stock of good i held by sector j,
$a_{ij}, b_{ij} =$ non-negative constants.

The above model is usually referred to as the *dynamic* Leontief model in order to distinguish it from an earlier static version of the model given in Leontief (1941).

Equations (8.2.1) assume that the current inputs of each sector are proportional to its output. Current inputs include not only the amounts of labour and materials used directly in the production process but also the amounts of various capital goods required for replacement. Thus, if sector i is the machine tool industry and sector j the motor-car industry, the volume of sales (per unit of time) of machine tools to the motor-car industry equals $Q_{ij} + DS_{ij}$, where Q_{ij} is the purchase for replacement and DS_{ij} the rate of addition to stocks.

For $j = 1, \ldots, n - 1$ the a_{ij}'s can be interpreted as technological coefficients. But for $j = n$ they should be interpreted as behaviour parameters. Thus, if relative prices are constant, the interpretation of the subset of equations (8.2.1) for $j = n$ is that a fixed proportion of household income is spent on each good. There is, of course, no reason why Leontief's technological assumptions should imply constant prices (see Solow (1959) and Hahn (1963) for models determining the dynamic behaviour of prices under a Leontief technology). If relative prices are not constant, then the subset of equations (8.2.1) for which $j = n$ assume that the household consumption of each good is proportional to the level of employment. Although rather unrealistic, this assumption leads to great simplifications. A particular feature of the Leontief model is that the equations determining the behaviour of inputs and outputs are separated from those determining prices. Here we shall confine our attention to the behaviour of inputs and outputs.

Equations (8.2.2) assume that the stocks held by each sector are proportional to its output. We have already noted that a sector's purchases of capital goods such as machine tools can be classified into current inputs and additions to stock. Its purchases of materials such as steel and cement can be similarly classified.

Equations (8.2.3) are equilibrium conditions. They assume that the output of each good equals the demand for it. The most realistic interpretation of these equations is that they are approximations to some sort of adjustment relations which tend to eliminate any differences between supply and demand. (In such adjustment relations the S_{ij}'s would denote desired stock levels.) But we shall see later that there are certain difficulties associated with this interpretation.

From equations (8.2.1) to (8.2.3) we obtain

$$Q = AQ + BDQ, \tag{8.2.4}$$

where Q is a column vector whose elements are the Q_i's, A is an $n \times n$ matrix whose elements are the a_{ij}'s, and B is an $n \times n$ matrix whose elements are the b_{ij}'s. It is clear, therefore, that the system has a stationary solution only if the $n \times n$ matrix $I - A$ is singular. But there is no economic reason why this matrix should be singular. We now assume, therefore, that $I - A$ is non-singular. We assume, moreover, that the elements of $(I - A)^{-1}$ are positive.

Since the elements of A are non-negative and $(I - A)^{-1} = \lim_{N \to \infty} \left(I + \sum_{r=1}^{N} A^r \right)$ provided that the latter limit exists, the elements of $(I - A)^{-1}$ are non-negative provided that $\sum_{r=1}^{N} A^r$ has a limit. If, in addition, A is irreducible (i.e. there is no subset of the indices $1, \ldots, n$ such that $a_{ij} = 0$ if j is in the subset and i is not in the subset) the elements of $(I - A)^{-1}$ must be positive. (See Solow (1952) for a discussion of these conditions and their economic interpretation.)

From (8.2.4) we obtain

$$Q = CDQ, \tag{8.2.5}$$

where $C = (I - A)^{-1}B$. Since each sector is assumed to hold a stock of at least one good, each column of B has at least one positive element. Hence the elements of C are positive. Now a matrix whose elements are positive has one, and only one, characteristic root associated with a vector whose elements are positive; and this root is greater than the modulus of any other characteristic root (see Gantmacher (1959), Ch. 13). Hence we have

$$CQ^* = \lambda^* Q^*, \tag{8.2.6}$$

where the elements of Q^* are positive and λ^* is greater than the modulus of any other characteristic root of C. It follows from (8.2.6) that (8.2.5) has a positive solution,

$$Q = Q^* e^{(1/\lambda^*)t}. \tag{8.2.7}$$

We refer to (8.2.7) as a *balanced growth path* since, on this path, all outputs grow at the same proportional rate, $1/\lambda^*$. Since λ^* is the only characteristic root associated with a characteristic vector whose elements are positive, the only balanced growth paths are those on which the outputs are proportional to the elements of Q^*.

It is clear that, if the initial outputs are not on a balanced growth path, but λ^* is the only positive characteristic root of C and the real parts of the reciprocals of all complex roots are less than $1/\lambda^*$, then the proportional deviations of the outputs from a balanced growth path must tend to zero as $t \to \infty$. But these conditions are not always satisfied, and when they are not the model fails to provide a realistic description of the behaviour of an economy. For its behaviour as $t \to \infty$ will then be dominated by the terms involving the characteristic root whose reciprocal has the greatest real part. If this root is complex there will be explosive oscillations and some output will, eventually, become negative, while if it is positive the associated characteristic sector has at least one negative element and, again, some output will eventually become negative.

A more serious weakness of the model, as a potential econometric model, has been revealed by Sargan (1958). We have already remarked that the most realistic interpretation of equations (8.2.3) is that they are approximations to some sort of adjustment relations which tend to eliminate differences between supply and demand. The use of equilibrium conditions as approximations to adjustment relations is a common procedure in the construction of economic models and has been employed in several of the models discussed in the earlier chapters. But it is a valid procedure only if the solution of the system containing the equilibrium conditions is a good approximation to the solution of the system containing the adjustment relations or, more precisely, if the difference between the solutions of the two systems tends to zero as the time-lags in the adjustment relations tend to zero (or, equivalently, as the speed of response parameters tend to infinity). Sargan (1958) showed that, for a wide class of plausible adjustment relations, the Leontief model does not satisfy this condition. Moreover, a plausible system of adjustment relations for which the condition is satisfied has not been found. Opinions as to what is plausible may, of course, differ. But here we follow Sargan in regarding an adjustment relation in which demand follows production rather than vice versa as implausible on the grounds that it implies that entrepreneurs are able to forecast demand exactly. Using this criterion Sargan (1961) rejected, as implausible, certain adjustment relations suggested by Leontief (1961).

A system of adjustment equations belonging to the class considered by Sargan (1958) can be written in the form

$$O_i Q_i = Q_i - \sum_{j=1}^{n} a_{ij} Q_j - \sum_{j=1}^{n} b_{ij} D Q_j \qquad (i = 1, \ldots, n), \tag{8.2.8}$$

where O_i is a linear combination of products of basic operators which produce lags of different length or the derivative with respect to time. Each of the O_i's is assumed to satisfy the following conditions:

(*a*) If O_i is applied to a constant the result is zero.

(*b*) If O_i is applied to an increasing function of time the result is negative.

(*c*) $O_i Q$ contains the leading term in the equation, this meaning the term that has the largest lead (if there is more than one term with the largest lead the leading term is the one that has the highest order derivative).

The operator $-k_i D^2$ is a simple example of an operator satisfying the above conditions. If we substitute $O_i = -k_i D^2$ into (8.2.8) we obtain the system of adjustment equations that are implied by the assumption that the rate of decrease in output is proportional to excess stocks. The even simpler operator $-k_i D$ does not satisfy condition (*c*); and Sargan (1958) gave a heuristic argument against the use of the relation obtained by substituting $O_i = -k_i D$ in (8.2.8).

We shall now illustrate Sargan's argument by considering the simple case in which the economy has only one sector and one good. The Leontief model then reduces to the model used by Domar (1946) and Harrod (1948). Equation (8.2.4) becomes

$$Q = aQ + bDQ, \tag{8.2.9}$$

where Q is the total output of the economy, $0 < a < 1$ and $b > 0$. The solution of (8.2.9) is

$$Q = Q(0)e^{(1-a)t/b}, \tag{8.2.10}$$

which implies that output grows at the constant proportional rate $\dfrac{1-a}{b}$.

Suppose now that (8.2.9) is replaced by the adjustment equation

$$D^2 Q = k(aQ + bDQ - Q), \tag{8.2.11}$$

where k is a positive constant. Then the behaviour of Q depends on the roots of

$$x^2 - kbx + k(1-a) = 0. \tag{8.2.12}$$

Both roots of (8.2.12) are positive, and, as k tends to infinity, the smaller root tends to $\dfrac{1-a}{b}$, while the larger root tends to infinity. Hence (8.2.10) is an approximation to a particular solution of (8.2.11). But any disturbance causes a rapid divergence from the path described by this solution.

Sargan's argument suggests that the Leontief model is not adapted to explaining and predicting the behaviour of a decentralised economy.

But it may, nevertheless, be a useful planning model. For this purpose the equations (8.2.2) are replaced by the inequalities

$$S_{ij} \geq b_{ij}Q_j \qquad (i = 1, \ldots, n) \quad (j = 1, \ldots, n), \tag{8.2.13}$$

and the paths of the variables determined by introducing certain planning objectives (see Dorfman, Samuelson and Solow (1958)).

CHAPTER 9

METHODS OF ESTIMATION

THE applicability of the models discussed in the preceding chapters depends on the possibility of estimating their parameters from empirical data. This means that it depends on the possibility of estimating the parameters of a system of stochastic differential equations from a set of discrete observations of the variables. We shall now consider this problem.

9.1 Systems of Linear Stochastic Differential and Difference Equations

We shall consider, in particular, the stochastic differential equation system

$$Dy(t) = Ay(t) + \zeta(t), \tag{9.1.1}$$

where A is an $n \times n$ matrix of parameters, $y(t)$ a vector of random functions which are observable at integral values of t and $\zeta(t)$ a vector of disturbances. The elements of $\zeta(t)$ are assumed to have the following properties:

$$E\left\{\int_{t_1}^{t_2} \zeta_i(t)\,dt\right\} = 0 \qquad (i = 1, \ldots, n), \tag{9.1.2}$$

$$E\left\{\int_{t_1}^{t_2} \zeta_i(t)\,dt \int_{t_1}^{t_2} \zeta_j(t)\,dt\right\} = \sigma_{ij}(t_2 - t_1) \qquad \begin{matrix}(i = 1, \ldots, n)\\(j = 1, \ldots, n),\end{matrix} \tag{9.1.3}$$

$$E\left\{\int_{t_1}^{t_2} \zeta_i(t)\,dt \int_{t_3}^{t_4} \zeta_j(t)\,dt\right\} = 0 \qquad \begin{matrix}(i = 1, \ldots, n)\\(j = 1, \ldots, n),\end{matrix} \tag{9.1.4}$$

where E denotes the expected value, $t_1 < t_2 < t_3 < t_4$ and the σ_{ij}'s are parameters, the σ_{ii}'s being positive. Equation (9.1.3) implies that the variance of the mean value assumed by $\zeta_i(t)$ over the interval (t_1, t_2) tends to infinity as $t_2 - t_1 \longrightarrow 0$. This leads to some difficulty in the interpretation of (9.1.1). The correct interpretation of (9.1.1) is that

$$y(t_2) - y(t_1) = A\int_{t_1}^{t_2} y(t)\,dt + \int_{t_1}^{t_2} \zeta(t)\,dt \tag{9.1.5}$$

holds for any interval (t_1, t_2) where the elements of $\int_{t_1}^{t_2} \zeta_i(t)\,dt$ satisfy (9.1.2) to (9.1.4). (See Bartlett (1955) for various concepts of stochastic integration.)

We assume that A has distinct characteristic roots $\lambda_1, \ldots, \lambda_n$, all of which have negative real parts. Let H be a matrix such that

$$(9.1.6) \qquad HAH^{-1} = \begin{bmatrix} \lambda_1 & 0 & . & . & . & 0 \\ 0 & \lambda_2 & . & . & . & 0 \\ . & . & . & . & . & . \\ 0 & 0 & . & . & . & \lambda_n \end{bmatrix} = \Lambda,$$

and let $w(t)$ be a vector of variables defined by the transformation

$$(9.1.7) \qquad w(t) = Hy(t).$$

Then, from (9.1.1), (9.1.6) and (9.1.7), we obtain

$$(9.1.8) \qquad Dw(t) = \Lambda w(t) + H\zeta(t),$$

whose solution is

$$(9.1.9) \qquad w(t) = \int_{-\infty}^{t} e^{\Lambda(t-r)} H\zeta(r)\, dr,$$

where

$$e^{\Lambda t} = \begin{bmatrix} e^{\lambda_1 t} & 0 & . & . & . & 0 \\ 0 & e^{\lambda_2 t} & . & . & . & 0 \\ . & . & . & . & . & . \\ 0 & 0 & . & . & . & e^{\lambda_n t} \end{bmatrix}.$$

Hence the solution of (9.1.1) is

$$(9.1.10) \qquad y(t) = \int_{-\infty}^{t} H^{-1} e^{\Lambda(t-r)} H\zeta(r)\, dr.$$

From (9.1.10) we obtain

$$(9.1.11) \qquad y(t) = By(t-1) + \xi(t),$$

where

$$(9.1.12) \qquad B = H^{-1} e^{\Lambda} H,$$

and

$$(9.1.13) \qquad \xi(t) = \int_{t-1}^{t} H^{-1} e^{\Lambda(t-r)} H\zeta(r)\, dr.$$

And, from (9.1.3) and (9.1.13), we obtain

$$(9.1.14) \qquad E\{\xi(t)\xi(t)'\} = \int_{0}^{1} H^{-1} e^{\Lambda r} H\Sigma\, H' e^{\Lambda r} (H')^{-1}\, dr = \Omega,$$

where Σ is an $n \times n$ matrix whose elements are the σ_{ij}'s.

If Σ is a diagonal matrix this does not imply that Ω is a diagonal matrix. Thus, even if the disturbances in the differential equation system (9.1.1) are uncorrelated, the disturbances in the difference equation system (9.1.11) are, generally, correlated. But, because of (9.1.4), $E\{\xi(t)\xi(t-r)'\}$ $(r = 1, 2, \ldots)$ is a zero matrix, so that the latter disturbances are, nevertheless, serially uncorrelated. If certain elements of A are zero, this does not imply that the corresponding elements of B are zero, except in the special case in which A is a reducible matrix. In that case (9.1.1) contains an independent sub-system involving only a certain subset of the variables, and (9.1.11) contains a corresponding independent sub-system. We shall assume that A is irreducible.

From (9.1.6) we obtain

$$A = H^{-1}\Lambda H, \tag{9.1.15}$$

and, from (9.1.12),

$$HB = e^{\Lambda}H. \tag{9.1.16}$$

It is clear, from (9.1.16), that the rows of H are the characteristic vectors of B, while the elements of Λ are the logarithms of the characteristic roots of B. Hence, if B is known, A can be deduced from (9.1.15).

The above results can be generalised to cover higher order systems. Instead of (9.1.1) we have the system

$$D^k y(t) = \sum_{r=1}^{k} A_r D^{k-r} y(t) + \zeta(t), \tag{9.1.17}$$

whose interpretation is similar to that of (9.1.1). A sequence of equi-spaced observations generated by (9.1.17) satisfies the system

$$y(t) = \sum_{r=1}^{k} B_r y(t-r) + \sum_{r=0}^{k-1} C_r \xi(t-r), \tag{9.1.18}$$

where the elements of $\xi(t)$ are serially uncorrelated (see Bartlett and Rajalakshman (1953) and Phillips (1959)).

9.2 A General Method

Let us suppose now that we have a sequence of observations, $y(0), y(1), y(2), \ldots, y(T)$, and consider the problem of estimating the parameters of (9.1.1). The results obtained in the previous section suggest an obvious procedure. This is first to obtain estimates of the parameters of (9.1.11) and then deduce from these the estimated parameters of (9.1.1).

One way of estimating the parameters of (9.1.11) is by least-squares regression. The least-squares estimator of B is given by

$$B^* = Y'Z(Z'Z)^{-1}, \tag{9.2.1}$$

where

$$Y' = [y(1), y(2), \ldots, y(T)],$$
$$Z' = [y(0), y(1), \ldots, y(T-1)].$$

Mann and Wald (1943) showed that if the elements of $\xi(t)$ have finite moments and the characteristic roots of B lie within the unit circle, then B^* is a consistent estimator of B. But, for the present purpose, it is an inefficient estimator. For it does not take into account the *a priori* restrictions on A.

If (9.1.1) is an econometric model many of the elements of A will be assumed, *a priori*, to be zeros. And there may, in addition, be other more complicated restrictions on A. These imply certain restrictions on B. But the form of these restrictions is very complex. Even if the only *a priori* restrictions are that certain elements of A are zero the implied restrictions on B cannot be expressed in terms of algebraic functions of its elements. This is clear from (9.1.15) and the fact that the elements of Λ are the logarithms of the characteristic roots of B. We shall now describe a procedure that is equivalent to estimating B subject to a set of restrictions which are approximations to the true restrictions and can be expressed in terms of rational functions. (See Bergstrom (1966) for a discussion of the extension of this procedure to higher order systems.)

The procedure makes use of the approximate model

$$(9.2.2) \quad y(t) - y(t-1) = A_1[0{\cdot}5\{y(t) + y(t-1)\}] + u(t) \qquad (t = 1, \ldots, T),$$

wherever A_1 satisfies the same *a priori* restrictions as A, and $u(t)$ is a vector of serially uncorrelated random variables with zero means and the covariance matrix Σ_1. This system is similar in form to (9.1.5) except that $\int_{t-1}^{t} y(t)\,dt$ is replaced by $0{\cdot}5\{y(t) + y(t-1)\}$. The matrices A_1 and Σ_1 are assumed to be such that the joint distribution of a sequence of observations generated by (9.2.2) most closely approximates (in some sense) the joint distribution of a sequence of observations generated by (9.1.1), or, equivalently, by (9.1.11). If there were no *a priori* restrictions on A and the integrals of the disturbances in (9.1.1) were normally distributed, the two distributions could be made identical by putting

$$(9.2.3) \qquad A_1 = 2(B - I)(B + I)^{-1},$$

$$(9.2.4) \qquad \Sigma_1 = (I - 0{\cdot}5A_1)\Omega(I - 0{\cdot}5A_1)',$$

and assuming the elements of $u(t)$ to be normally distributed. This can be seen by comparing (9.1.11) with

$$(9.2.5) \quad \begin{aligned} y(t) &= (I - 0{\cdot}5A_1)^{-1}(I + 0{\cdot}5A_1)y(t-1) + (I - 0{\cdot}5A_1)^{-1}u(t) \\ &= B_1 y(t-1) + v(t) \qquad (t = 1, \ldots, T), \end{aligned}$$

which obtained from (9.2.2). It should be noted, however, that, even in this case, $A_1 \neq A$. Assuming that there are restrictions on A, and hence on A_1, the two distributions cannot be made identical.

It follows from the definition of B_1 in (9.2.5) that

$$(9.2.6) \qquad A_1 = 2(B_1 - I)(B_1 + I)^{-1}.$$

It is clear from (9.2.6) that the restrictions on B_1 implied by a set of linear restrictions on the elements of A_1 can be expressed in terms of rational functions of the elements of B_1. These restrictions can be regarded as approximations to the restrictions on B.

Now let $\hat{A}_1$ be a matrix whose elements are functions of the observations of the variables and which would be a consistent estimator of A_1 if the observations had been generated by (9.2.2). And let $\hat{B}_1$ be defined by

(9.2.7) $$\hat{B}_1 = (I - 0{\cdot}5\hat{A}_1)^{-1}(I + 0{\cdot}5\hat{A}_1).$$

Then, if the observations had been generated by (9.2.2), $\hat{B}_1$ would be a consistent estimator of B_1.

We shall now regard $\hat{B}_1$ as an estimator of B. It cannot be a consistent estimator of B since the restrictions that have been imposed on $\hat{B}_1$ are only approximately satisfied by B. Hence, since B^* is a consistent estimator of B, it must be preferred to $\hat{B}_1$ if the sample size is sufficiently large. But the elements of $\hat{B}_1$ can be expected to have smaller variances than the corresponding elements of B^* since the latter are unrestricted. A numerical example studied in Bergstrom (1966) suggests that, for samples of 100 quarterly observations generated by a realistic econometric model, this difference between the variances will be much more important than the asymptotic bias in $\hat{B}_1$.

From $\hat{B}_1$ we can obtain an estimator of A. This is given by

(9.2.8) $$\hat{A} = \hat{H}^{-1}\hat{\Lambda}\hat{H},$$

where

$$\hat{\Lambda} = \begin{bmatrix} \hat{\lambda}_1 & 0 & . & . & . & 0 \\ 0 & \hat{\lambda}_2 & . & . & . & 0 \\ . & . & . & . & . & . \\ 0 & . & . & . & . & \hat{\lambda}_n \end{bmatrix}$$

and the $\hat{\lambda}_i$'s and $\hat{H}$ satisfy:

(9.2.9) $$| \hat{B}_1 - e^{\hat{\lambda}_i}I | = 0,$$

(9.2.10) $$\hat{H}\hat{B}_1\hat{H}^{-1} = \begin{bmatrix} e^{\hat{\lambda}_1} & 0 & . & . & . & 0 \\ 0 & e^{\hat{\lambda}_2} & . & . & . & 0 \\ . & . & . & . & . & . \\ 0 & 0 & . & . & . & e^{\hat{\lambda}_n} \end{bmatrix}.$$

A more direct procedure would be to use $\hat{A}_1$ as an estimator of A. But there is a good reason for believing that $\hat{A}_1$ will not, usually, be as good an estimator as $\hat{A}$. This is that, even if there are no *a priori* restrictions on A, $\hat{A}_1$ is not a consistent estimator of A, whereas, in this case, $\hat{B}_1$ is a consistent estimator of B. The conjecture that $\hat{A}$ will usually be superior to $\hat{A}_1$ as an estimator of A is supported by the results obtained for the example referred to above (see Bergstrom (1966)).

The main practical difficulty in obtaining $\hat{A}$ is that of finding an $\hat{A}_1$ which would be a consistent estimator of A_1 if (9.2.2) were the true model. Least-squares regression of $y(t) - y(t-1)$ on $0{\cdot}5\{y(t) + y(t-1)\}$ does not provide a consistent estimator because of the presence of $y(t)$ in the latter vector. The model (9.2.2) is, in fact, a particular example of a more general type of model which was proposed by Haavelmo (1943) and has, since, been extensively discussed in the conometric literature. The final section of this chapter will be devoted a very brief discussion of this type of model and methods of obtaining sistent estimates of its parameters. The methods are discussed more in several recent textbooks on econometrics (see Johnston (1963), berger (1964) and Malinvaud (1964)).

e Simultaneous Equations Model

The general type of model referred to at the end of the preceding section can be written in the form

(9.3.1) $$Fy(t) + Gz(t) = u(t) \qquad (t = 1, \ldots, T),$$

where $z(t)' = [y(t-1)', y(t-2)', \ldots, y(t-k)', \bar{z}(t)']$, $y(t)$ is an $n \times 1$ vector of observable random variables called endogenous variables, $\bar{z}(t)$ is an $m \times 1$ vector of observable non-random variables called exogenous variables, F is an $n \times n$ matrix of parameters, G is an $n \times (kn + m)$ matrix of parameters and $u(t)$ is an $n \times 1$ vector of random disturbances which are assumed to have the following properties:

(9.3.2) $$E\{u(t)\} = 0 \qquad (t = 1, \ldots, T),$$

(9.3.3) $$E\{u(t)u(t)'\} = \Sigma \qquad (t = 1, \ldots, T),$$

(9.3.4) $$E\{u(t_1)u(t_2)'\} = 0 \qquad (t_1 = 1, \ldots, T),\ (t_2 = 1, \ldots, T),\ (t_1 \neq t_2).$$

We assume also that the initial vectors $y(1-k), y(2-k), \ldots, y(0)$ are fixed. Thus the elements of these vectors and the vectors $\bar{z}(1), \bar{z}(2), \ldots, \bar{z}(T)$ are assumed to be given numbers. Finally, we assume certain linear restrictions on the elements of F and G. The model (9.2.2) is clearly a special case of the above model with $k = 1$ and $m = 0$.

With reference to any particular time period (i.e. any particular value of t) the elements of $y(t)$ are called *jointly dependent variables*, while the elements of $z(t)$ are called *predetermined variables*. Assuming that F is non-singular, the equations (9.3.1) relating to each time period can be solved for the jointly dependent variables, yielding

(9.3.5) $$y(t) = Bz(t) + v(t) \qquad (t = 1, \ldots, T),$$

where

(9.3.6) $$B = -F^{-1}G,$$

The main practical difficulty in obtaining $\hat{A}$ is that of finding an $\hat{A}_1$ which would be a consistent estimator of A_1 if (9.2.2) were the true model. Least-squares regression of $y(t) - y(t-1)$ on $0{\cdot}5\{y(t) + y(t-1)\}$ does not provide a consistent estimator because of the presence of $y(t)$ in the latter vector. The model (9.2.2) is, in fact, a particular example of a more general type of model which was proposed by Haavelmo (1943) and has, since, been extensively discussed in the econometric literature. The final section of this chapter will be devoted to a very brief discussion of this type of model and methods of obtaining consistent estimates of its parameters. The methods are discussed more fully in several recent textbooks on econometrics (see Johnston (1963), Goldberger (1964) and Malinvaud (1964)).

9.3 The Simultaneous Equations Model

The general type of model referred to at the end of the preceding section can be written in the form

$$Fy(t) + Gz(t) = u(t) \qquad (t = 1, \ldots, T), \tag{9.3.1}$$

where $z(t)' = [y(t-1)', y(t-2)', \ldots, y(t-k)', \bar{z}(t)']$, $y(t)$ is an $n \times 1$ vector of observable random variables called endogenous variables, $\bar{z}(t)$ is an $m \times 1$ vector of observable non-random variables called exogenous variables, F is an $n \times n$ matrix of parameters, G is an $n \times (kn + m)$ matrix of parameters and $u(t)$ is an $n \times 1$ vector of random disturbances which are assumed to have the following properties:

$$E\{u(t)\} = 0 \qquad (t = 1, \ldots, T), \tag{9.3.2}$$

$$E\{u(t)u(t)'\} = \Sigma \qquad (t = 1, \ldots, T), \tag{9.3.3}$$

$$E\{u(t_1)u(t_2)'\} = 0 \qquad (t_1 = 1, \ldots, T)\ (t_2 = 1, \ldots, T)\ (t_1 \neq t_2). \tag{9.3.4}$$

We assume also that the initial vectors $y(1-k), y(2-k), \ldots, y(0)$ are fixed. Thus the elements of these vectors and the vectors $\bar{z}(1), \bar{z}(2), \ldots, \bar{z}(T)$ are assumed to be given numbers. Finally, we assume certain linear restrictions on the elements of F and G. The model (9.2.2) is clearly a special case of the above model with $k = 1$ and $m = 0$.

With reference to any particular time period (i.e. any particular value of t) the elements of $y(t)$ are called *jointly dependent variables*, while the elements of $z(t)$ are called *predetermined variables*. Assuming that F is non-singular, the equations (9.3.1) relating to each time period can be solved for the jointly dependent variables, yielding

$$y(t) = Bz(t) + v(t) \qquad (t = 1, \ldots, T), \tag{9.3.5}$$

where

$$B = -F^{-1}G, \tag{9.3.6}$$

…).

…ve obtain

$(t = 1, \ldots, T)$,

…$^{-1}\Sigma(F')^{-1}$ $(t = 1, \ldots, T)$,

$(t_1 = 1, \ldots, T)$ $(t_2 = 1, \ldots, T)$ $(t_1 \neq t_2)$.

… to (9.3.10) is known as the

… the joint frequency function … let $\phi_t(y(t)' \mid y(1)', y(2)', \ldots,$ … equency function of the ele… …ts of $y(1), y(2), \ldots, y(t-1)$.

… $\frac{f_T - 1}{f_T - 2} \cdots \frac{f_2}{f_1} \cdot f_1$

…$' \mid y(1)', y(2)', \ldots, y(t-1)')$.

…ng (9.3.2) to (9.3.4), the ele… …istributed. Then, because of …re also normally distributed, …0), we obtain

…$') =$

…$Bz(t)\}'\Omega^{-1}\{y(t) - Bz(t)\}]$

…$z(t)'B'\}\Omega^{-1}\{y(t) - Bz(t)\}]$,

…. Then, from (9.3.11) and

…$z(t)'B'\}\Omega^{-1}\{y(t) - Bz(t)\}]$

…$^{-1}\{Y' - BZ'\}]$,

…$y(T)]$,

…$z(T)]$,

… distribution of the values …e periods 1 to T is uniquely determined by the values assumed by these variables over the periods $1 - k$ to 0, the values assumed by the exogenous variables over the periods 1 to T and the matrices of reduced form parameters, B and Ω. Conversely, there is only one set of reduced form parameters which, together with the given initial values of the endogenous variables and given values of the exogenous variables, yields a particular joint normal distribution of the values assumed by the endogenous variables over the periods 1 to T. For $Bz(t)$ is the vector of conditional means and Ω the conditional covariance matrix of the elements of $y(t)$ for given values of the elements of $y(1), y(2), \ldots, y(t-1)$.

Now let us consider further the relation between the structural parameters (i.e. the elements of F, G and Σ) and the reduced form parameters. From (9.3.6) and (9.3.9) we have

$$FB = -G, \tag{9.3.14}$$

$$\Sigma = F\Omega F'. \tag{9.3.15}$$

The relation (9.3.14) comprises $n(nk + m)$ linear equations in the $n\{n(k+1) + m\}$ elements of F and G. We shall distinguish two cases, depending on the number and form of the *a priori* restrictions on F and G. We assume that there are no *a priori* restrictions on Σ.

Case 1

In this case there are infinitely many sets of values of the structural parameters satisfying (9.3.14) and the *a priori* restrictions. Hence, even if the joint frequency function, $f_T(y(1)', y(2)', \ldots, y(T)')$ were known, we could not deduce the true values of all the structural parameters. If there are any structural parameters which are uniquely determined by (9.3.14), (9.3.15) and the *a priori* restrictions (and hence could be deduced from $f_T(y(1)', y(2)', \ldots, y(T)')$), then these parameters are said to be *identifiable*, while the remaining structural parameters are said to be *not identifiable*.

Case 2

In this case there is one, and only one, set of values of the structural parameters satisfying (9.3.14), (9.3.15) and the *a priori* restrictions. Hence all of the structural parameters are identifiable. We can distinguish two sub-cases:

(a) where the *a priori* restrictions on F and G together, with the requirement that (9.3.14) has a solution, do not restrict B;
(b) where these conditions do restrict B.

In case 2(a) the *a priori* restrictions are said to be *just-identifying*, while in case 2(b) they are said to be *over-identifying*.

Considering, now, the model (9.2.2), it is clear from (9.2.6) that, in the

It is clear from (9.2.6) that the restrictions on B_1 implied by a set of linear restrictions on the elements of A_1 can be expressed in terms of rational functions of the elements of B_1. These restrictions can be regarded as approximations to the restrictions on B.

Now let $\hat{A}_1$ be a matrix whose elements are functions of the observations of the variables and which would be a consistent estimator of A_1 if the observations had been generated by (9.2.2). And let $\hat{B}_1$ be defined by

$$\hat{B}_1 = (I - 0{\cdot}5\hat{A}_1)^{-1}(I + 0{\cdot}5\hat{A}_1). \tag{9.2.7}$$

Then, if the observations had been generated by (9.2.2), $\hat{B}_1$ would be a consistent estimator of B_1.

We shall now regard $\hat{B}_1$ as an estimator of B. It cannot be a consistent estimator of B since the restrictions that have been imposed on $\hat{B}_1$ are only approximately satisfied by B. Hence, since B^* is a consistent estimator of B, it must be preferred to $\hat{B}_1$ if the sample size is sufficiently large. But the elements of $\hat{B}_1$ can be expected to have smaller variances than the corresponding elements of B^* since the latter are unrestricted. A numerical example studied in Bergstrom (1966) suggests that, for samples of 100 quarterly observations generated by a realistic econometric model, this difference between the variances will be much more important than the asymptotic bias in $\hat{B}_1$.

From $\hat{B}_1$ we can obtain an estimator of A. This is given by

$$\hat{A} = \hat{H}^{-1}\hat{\Lambda}\hat{H}, \tag{9.2.8}$$

where

$$\hat{\Lambda} = \begin{bmatrix} \hat{\lambda}_1 & 0 & . & . & . & 0 \\ 0 & \hat{\lambda}_2 & . & . & . & 0 \\ . & . & . & . & . & . \\ 0 & . & . & . & . & \hat{\lambda}_n \end{bmatrix}$$

and the $\hat{\lambda}_i$'s and $\hat{H}$ satisfy:

$$| \hat{B}_1 - e^{\hat{\lambda}_i} I | = 0, \tag{9.2.9}$$

$$\hat{H}\hat{B}_1\hat{H}^{-1} = \begin{bmatrix} e^{\hat{\lambda}_1} & 0 & . & . & . & 0 \\ 0 & e^{\hat{\lambda}_2} & . & . & . & 0 \\ . & . & . & . & . & . \\ 0 & 0 & . & . & . & e^{\hat{\lambda}_n} \end{bmatrix}. \tag{9.2.10}$$

A more direct procedure would be to use $\hat{A}_1$ as an estimator of A. But there is a good reason for believing that $\hat{A}_1$ will not, usually, be as good an estimator as $\hat{A}$. This is that, even if there are no *a priori* restrictions on A, $\hat{A}_1$ is not a consistent estimator of A, whereas, in this case, $\hat{B}_1$ is a consistent estimator of B. The conjecture that $\hat{A}$ will usually be superior to $\hat{A}_1$ as an estimator of A is supported by the results obtained for the example referred to above (see Bergstrom (1966)).

The main practical difficulty in obtaining $\hat{A}$ is that of finding an $\hat{A}_1$ which would be a consistent estimator of A_1 if (9.2.2) were the true model. Least-squares regression of $y(t) - y(t-1)$ on $0{\cdot}5\{y(t) + y(t-1)\}$ does not provide a consistent estimator because of the presence of $y(t)$ in the latter vector. The model (9.2.2) is, in fact, a particular example of a more general type of model which was proposed by Haavelmo (1943) and has, since, been extensively discussed in the econometric literature. The final section of this chapter will be devoted to a very brief discussion of this type of model and methods of obtaining consistent estimates of its parameters. The methods are discussed more fully in several recent textbooks on econometrics (see Johnston (1963), Goldberger (1964) and Malinvaud (1964)).

9.3 The Simultaneous Equations Model

The general type of model referred to at the end of the preceding section can be written in the form

$$Fy(t) + Gz(t) = u(t) \qquad (t = 1, \ldots, T), \tag{9.3.1}$$

where $z(t)' = [y(t-1)', y(t-2)', \ldots, y(t-k)', \bar{z}(t)']$, $y(t)$ is an $n \times 1$ vector of observable random variables called endogenous variables, $\bar{z}(t)$ is an $m \times 1$ vector of observable non-random variables called exogenous variables, F is an $n \times n$ matrix of parameters, G is an $n \times (kn + m)$ matrix of parameters and $u(t)$ is an $n \times 1$ vector of random disturbances which are assumed to have the following properties:

$$E\{u(t)\} = 0 \qquad (t = 1, \ldots, T), \tag{9.3.2}$$

$$E\{u(t)u(t)'\} = \Sigma \qquad (t = 1, \ldots, T), \tag{9.3.3}$$

$$E\{u(t_1)u(t_2)'\} = 0 \qquad (t_1 = 1, \ldots, T)\ (t_2 = 1, \ldots, T)\ (t_1 \neq t_2). \tag{9.3.4}$$

We assume also that the initial vectors $y(1-k), y(2-k), \ldots, y(0)$ are fixed. Thus the elements of these vectors and the vectors $\bar{z}(1), \bar{z}(2), \ldots, \bar{z}(T)$ are assumed to be given numbers. Finally, we assume certain linear restrictions on the elements of F and G. The model (9.2.2) is clearly a special case of the above model with $k = 1$ and $m = 0$.

With reference to any particular time period (i.e. any particular value of t) the elements of $y(t)$ are called *jointly dependent variables*, while the elements of $z(t)$ are called *predetermined variables*. Assuming that F is non-singular, the equations (9.3.1) relating to each time period can be solved for the jointly dependent variables, yielding

$$y(t) = Bz(t) + v(t) \qquad (t = 1, \ldots, T), \tag{9.3.5}$$

where

$$B = -F^{-1}G, \tag{9.3.6}$$

$$v(t) = F^{-1}u(t). \tag{9.3.7}$$

And, from (9.3.2) to (9.3.4) and (9.3.7), we obtain

$$E\{v(t)\} = 0 \qquad (t = 1, \ldots, T), \tag{9.3.8}$$

$$E\{v(t)v(t)'\} = \Omega = F^{-1}\Sigma(F')^{-1} \qquad (t = 1, \ldots, T), \tag{9.3.9}$$

$$E\{v(t_1)v(t_2)'\} = 0 \qquad \begin{matrix}(t_1 = 1, \ldots, T) \\ (t_2 = 1, \ldots, T) \\ (t_1 \neq t_2).\end{matrix} \tag{9.3.10}$$

The system (9.3.5) together with (9.3.8) to (9.3.10) is known as the *reduced form* of the model.

Now let $f_t(y(1)', y(2)', \ldots, y(t)')$ denote the joint frequency function of the elements of $y(1), y(2), \ldots, y(t)$, and let $\phi_t(y(t)' \mid y(1)', y(2)', \ldots, y(t-1)')$ denote the joint conditional frequency function of the elements of $y(t)$ for given values of the elements of $y(1), y(2), \ldots, y(t-1)$. Then we have

$$\begin{aligned} f_T(y(1)', y(2)', \ldots, y(T)') &= \frac{f_T}{f_T - 1} \cdot \frac{f_T - 1}{f_T - 2} \cdots \frac{f_2}{f_1} \cdot f_1 \\ &= \prod_{t=1}^{T} \phi_t(y(t)' \mid y(1)', y(2)', \ldots, y(t-1)'). \end{aligned} \tag{9.3.11}$$

Suppose now that, in addition to satisfying (9.3.2) to (9.3.4), the elements of $u(t)(t = 1, \ldots, T)$ are normally distributed. Then, because of (9.3.7), the elements of $v(t)(t = 1, \ldots, T)$ are also normally distributed, and, using (9.3.5), (9.3.8), (9.3.9) and (9.3.10), we obtain

$$\begin{aligned} &\phi_t(y(t)' \mid y(1)', y(2)', \ldots, y(t-1)') = \\ &= 2\pi^{-n/2} \mid \Omega \mid^{-1/2} \exp[-\tfrac{1}{2}\{y(t) - Bz(t)\}'\Omega^{-1}\{y(t) - Bz(t)\}] \\ &= 2\pi^{-n/2} \mid \Omega \mid^{-1/2} \exp[-\tfrac{1}{2}\{y(t)' - z(t)'B'\}\Omega^{-1}\{y(t) - Bz(t)\}], \end{aligned} \tag{9.3.12}$$

where $\mid \Omega \mid$ denotes the determinant of Ω. Then, from (9.3.11) and (9.3.12), we obtain

$$\begin{aligned} &f_T(y(1)', y(2)', \ldots, y(T)') = \\ &= 2\pi^{-nT/2} \mid \Omega \mid^{-T/2} \exp\left[-\tfrac{1}{2}\sum_{t=1}^{T}\{y(t)' - z(t)'B'\}\Omega^{-1}\{y(t) - Bz(t)\}\right] \\ &= 2\pi^{-nT/2} \mid \Omega \mid^{-T/2} \exp[-\tfrac{1}{2} tr\{Y - ZB'\}\Omega^{-1}\{Y' - BZ'\}], \end{aligned} \tag{9.3.13}$$

where

$$Y' = [y(1), y(2), \ldots, y(T)],$$
$$Z' = [z(1), z(2), \ldots, z(T)],$$

and *tr* denotes the trace of a matrix.

Equation (9.3.13) shows that the joint distribution of the values assumed by the endogenous variables over the periods 1 to T is uniquely

determined by the values assumed by these variables over the periods $1 - k$ to 0, the values assumed by the exogenous variables over the periods 1 to T and the matrices of reduced form parameters, B and Ω. Conversely, there is only one set of reduced form parameters which, together with the given initial values of the endogenous variables and given values of the exogenous variables, yields a particular joint normal distribution of the values assumed by the endogenous variables over the periods 1 to T. For $Bz(t)$ is the vector of conditional means and Ω the conditional covariance matrix of the elements of $y(t)$ for given values of the elements of $y(1), y(2), \ldots, y(t-1)$.

Now let us consider further the relation between the structural parameters (i.e. the elements of F, G and Σ) and the reduced form parameters. From (9.3.6) and (9.3.9) we have

$$FB = -G, \tag{9.3.14}$$

$$\Sigma = F\Omega F'. \tag{9.3.15}$$

The relation (9.3.14) comprises $n(nk + m)$ linear equations in the $n\{n(k + 1) + m\}$ elements of F and G. We shall distinguish two cases, depending on the number and form of the *a priori* restrictions on F and G. We assume that there are no *a priori* restrictions on Σ.

Case 1

In this case there are infinitely many sets of values of the structural parameters satisfying (9.3.14) and the *a priori* restrictions. Hence, even if the joint frequency function, $f_T(y(1)', y(2)', \ldots, y(T)')$ were known, we could not deduce the true values of all the structural parameters. If there are any structural parameters which are uniquely determined by (9.3.14), (9.3.15) and the *a priori* restrictions (and hence could be deduced from $f_T(y(1)', y(2)', \ldots, y(T)')$), then these parameters are said to be *identifiable*, while the remaining structural parameters are said to be *not identifiable*.

Case 2

In this case there is one, and only one, set of values of the structural parameters satisfying (9.3.14), (9.3.15) and the *a priori* restrictions. Hence all of the structural parameters are identifiable. We can distinguish two sub-cases:

(a) where the *a priori* restrictions on F and G together, with the requirement that (9.3.14) has a solution, do not restrict B;
(b) where these conditions do restrict B.

In case 2(a) the *a priori* restrictions are said to be *just-identifying*, while in case 2(b) they are said to be *over-identifying*.

Considering, now, the model (9.2.2), it is clear from (9.2.6) that, in the

special case in which there are no *a priori* restrictions on A_1, the restrictions implicit in the form of (9.2.2) are just-identifying, and all the parameters are identifiable. But, if there are some *a priori* restrictions on A_1 these restrictions are over-identifying. For they restrict B_1 which corresponds to B in the more general model under discussion in this section. Thus case 2(b) is the one in which we are particularly interested. It is also the case that has most commonly occurred when models of actual economies have been directly formulated as simultaneous equations models (see, for example, Klein and Goldberger (1955)). We assume from now on, therefore, that the *a priori* restrictions are over-identifying.

From (9.3.9) we obtain:

$$|\Omega| = |F|^{-2}|\Sigma| \tag{9.3.16}$$

$$\Omega^{-1} = F'\Sigma^{-1}F. \tag{9.3.17}$$

Then from (9.3.6), (9.3.13), (9.3.16) and (9.3.17), we obtain:

$$f_T(y(1)', y(2)', \ldots, y(T)') = 2\pi^{-nT/2}\,\|F\|^T\,|\Sigma|^{-T/2}\exp\left[-\tfrac{1}{2}\operatorname{tr}\{YF' + ZG'\}\Sigma^{-1}\{FY' + GZ'\}\right] \tag{9.3.18}$$

where $\|F\|$ denotes the modulus of $|F|$. Equation (9.3.18) expresses the joint frequency function of the values assumed by the endogenous variables over periods 1 to T in a form in which its parameters are the structural parameters of the model, the initial values of the endogenous variables and the values of the exogenous variables. If we substitute into this function the observed values of all the variables over the periods $1 - k$ to T we obtain a likelihood function whose arguments are the structural parameters of the model. Let $L(F, G, \Sigma)$ denote the logarithm of this function. Then

$$L(F, G, \Sigma) = \frac{-nT}{2}\log 2\pi + T\log\|F\| + \frac{T}{2}\log|\Sigma^{-1}| - \tfrac{1}{2}\operatorname{tr}\{YF' + ZG'\}\Sigma^{-1}\{FY' + GZ'\}. \tag{9.3.19}$$

The values of the structural parameters that maximise $L(F, G, \Sigma)$ subject to the *a priori* restrictions are called *full-information maximum-likelihood* estimates of the parameters. Computational procedures for obtaining these estimates are described in Koopmans, Rubin and Leipnik (1950), Chernoff and Divinsky (1953), Brown (1959), Eisenpress (1962) and Durbin (1963). All of these procedures are iterative. For, even if the only *a priori* restrictions on F and G are that certain elements are unity and others zero, the equations obtained by equating to zero the partial derivatives of $L(F, G, \Sigma)$ with respect to F, G and Σ^{-1} are rather awkward non-linear equations.

It is well known that, if a joint probability distribution satisfies certain regularity conditions, maximum-likelihood estimates of its parameters from a set of independent observations of the variables are consistent, asymptotically normal and asymptotically efficient (see Cramér (1951)). But this result does not imply that the full-information maximum-likelihood estimates of the parameters of the above model have these properties. For the vectors $y(1), y(2), \ldots, y(T)$ are not independent. Nevertheless, Mann and Wald (1943) showed that, if (9.3.1) contains no exogenous variables except a vector of constants, and its parameters are such that the variables would tend to limits if there were no disturbances, then, provided that the disturbances have finite moments of a sufficiently high order, the estimates obtained by maximising $L(F, G, \Sigma)$ subject to the *a priori* restrictions are consistent and asymptotically normal. It should be noted that these results hold even if the disturbances are not normally distributed, although, in this case, the estimates would not be maximum-likelihood estimates. The results obtained by Mann and Wald can be extended to the case in which (9.3.1) does contain exogenous variables under certain assumptions about the behaviour of these variables (see Koopmans, Rubin and Leipnik (1950)).

Because of the heavy computational cost of obtaining full-information maximum-likelihood estimates much effort has been devoted to the development of simpler estimates and the study of their properties. Even if full-information maximum-likelihood estimates are to be computed, simpler estimates are useful as a starting-point for the iterative procedure.

A method due to Anderson and Rubin (1949) and known as the *limited-information maximum-likelihood method* can be applied to the individual structural equations separately, but utilises observations of variables not occurring in the equation whose parameters are being estimated. The application of this method to a particular structural equation involves the maximisation of a likelihood function subject to the *a priori* restrictions relating to the parameters of that equation only. The computational procedure is non-iterative except for the computation of the smallest characteristic root of a certain matrix. Limited-information maximum-likelihood estimates are consistent and asymptotically normal under the same conditions as full-information maximum-likelihood estimates (see Anderson and Rubin (1950)), but are less efficient than the latter.

There is an even simpler method due to Theil (1953 and 1961) and Basmann (1957) and known as *two-stage least-squares*. The first step is to estimate the reduced form equations by least-squares regression ignoring all *a priori* restrictions. The next step is to replace the observed values of the jointly dependent variables in each structural equation by the values computed from the estimated reduced form equations and then estimate the structural parameters by least-squares regression. The limited-information maximum-likelihood and two-stage least-square methods use the same amount of *a priori* information and yield estimates that have the same asymptotic normal distribution (see Basmann (1960)).

Finally, there is a more complicated non-iterative method due to Zellner and Theil (1962) and known as *three-stage least-squares*. This method involves the application of Aitken's method of generalised least-squares to a transformed system making use of the two-stage least-squares estimates of the elements of Σ. The full-information maximum-likelihood and three-stage least-squares methods each make full use of the *a priori* restrictions on F and G, and they yield estimates that have the same asymptotic normal distribution (see Madansky (1964), Rothenberg and Leenders (1964) and Sargan (1964)). But little is known, yet, about the small sample properties of these estimates.

REFERENCES

Allen, R. G. D. (1956, second edition 1959): *Mathematical Economics*, Macmillan, London.

Anderson, T. W. and Rubin, H. (1949): "Estimation of the Parameters of a Single Equation in a Complete System of Stochastic Equations", *Annals of Mathematical Statistics*, **20**, 46–63.

Anderson, T. W. and Rubin, H. (1950): "The Asymptotic Properties of Estimates of the Parameters of a Single Equation in a Complete System of Stochastic Equations", *Annals of Mathematical Statistics*, **21**, 570–82.

Arrow, K. J. (1962): "The Economic Implications of Learning by Doing", *Review of Economic Studies*, **29**, 155–73.

Arrow, K. J., Block, H. D. and Hurwicz, L. (1959): "On the Stability of Competitive Equilibrium, II", *Econometrica*, **27**, 82–109.

Arrow, K. J., Chenery, H. B., Minhas, B. and Solow, R. M. (1961): "Capital, Substitution and Economic Efficiency", *Review of Economics and Statistics*, **43**, 225–50.

Arrow, K. J. and Debreu, G. (1954): "Existence of an Equilibrium for a Competitive Economy", *Econometrica*, **22**, 265–90.

Bartlett, M. S. (1955): *An Introduction to Stochastic Processes*, Cambridge University Press.

Bartlett, M. S. and Rajalakshman, D. V. (1953): "Goodness of Fit Tests for Simultaneous Autoregressive Series", *Journal of the Royal Statistical Society*, **B**, **15**, 107–24.

Basmann, R. L. (1957): "A Generalized Classical Method of Linear Estimation of Coefficients in a Structural Equation", *Econometrica*, **25**, 77–83.

Basmann, R. L. (1960): "On the Asymptotic Distribution of Generalised Linear Estimators", *Econometrica*, **28**, 97–108.

Bergstrom, A. R. (1962): "A Model of Technical Progress the Production Function and Cyclical Growth", *Economica*, **29**, 357–70.

Bergstrom, A. R. (1966): "Nonrecursive Models as Discrete Approximations to Systems of Stochastic Differential Equations", *Econometrica*, **34**, 173–82.

Bronfenbrenner, M. and Mayer, T. (1960): "Liquidity Functions in the American Economy", *Econometrica* **28**, 810–34.

Brown T. M. (1959): "Simplified Full Maximum-Likelihood and Comparative Structural Estimates", *Econometrica* **27**, 638–53.

Chernoff H. and Divinsky, N. (1953): "The Computation of Maximum-Likelihood Estimates of Linear Structural Equations", Chapter 10 of *Studies in Econometric Method*, ed. W. C. Hood and T. C. Koopmans, Wiley, New York.

Cramér, H. (1951): *Mathematical Methods of Statistics*, Princeton University Press.

Domar, E. D. (1946): "Capital Expansion, Rate of Growth and Employment", *Econometrica,* **14**, 137–47.

Dorfman, R. Samuelson, P. A. and Solow, R. M. (1958): *Linear Programming and Economic Analysis* McGraw-Hill, New York.

Durbin, J. (1963): "Maximum-Likelihood Estimation of the Parameters of a System of Simultaneous Regression Equations", presented at European Meeting of Econometric Society, Copenhagen, (to be published).

Eisenpress, H. (1962): "Note on the Computation of Full-Information Maximum-Likelihood Estimates of Coefficients of a Simultaneous System", *Econometrica,* **30**, 343–8.

Friedman, M. (1957): *A Theory of the Consumption Function,* National Bureau of Economic Research, (distr. Princeton University Press).

Gantmacher, F. (1959, translated from Russian), *Theory of Matrices,* (K. A. Hirsch tr.), Chelsea Publishing Co., New York.

Goldberger, A. S. (1964): *Econometric Theory,* Wiley, New York.

Goodwin, R. M. (1951): "The Nonlinear Accelerator and the Persistence of Business Cycles", *Econometrica,* **19**, 1–17.

Gorman, W. M. (1953): "Community Preference Fields", *Econometrica,* **21**, 63–80.

Haavelmo, T. (1943): "The Statistical Implications of a System of Simultaneous Equations", *Econometrica,* **11**, 1–12.

Hahn, F. H. (1963): "On the Disequilibrium Behaviour of a Multi-Sectorial Growth Model", *Economic Journal,* **73**, 442–57.

Harrod, R. F. (1948): *Towards a Dynamic Economics,* Macmillan, London.

Hicks, J. R. (1932): *The Theory of Wages,* Macmillan, London.

Hicks, J. R. (1938, second edition 1946): *Value and Capital,* Oxford University Press.

Hicks, J. R. (1950): *A Contribution to the Theory of the Trade Cycle,* Oxford University Press.

Johansen, L. (1959): "Substitution versus Fixed Production Coefficients in the Theory of Economic Growth: A Synthesis", *Econometrica,* **27**, 157–76.

Johnston, J. (1963): *Econometric Methods,* McGraw-Hill, New York.

Kaldor, N. and Mirrlees, J. A. (1962): "A New Model of Economic Growth", *Review of Economic Studies,* **29**, 174–92.

Keynes, J. M. (1936): *The General Theory of Employment Interest and Money,* Macmillan, London.

Klein, L. R. and Goldberger, A. S. (1955): *An Econometric Model of the United States 1929–1952,* North-Holland Publishing Company, Amsterdam.

Koopmans, T. C., Rubin, H. and Leipnik, R. B. (1950): "Measuring Equation Systems in Dynamic Economics", Chapter 2 of *Statistical Inference in Dynamic Economic Models,* ed. T. C. Koopmans, Wiley, New York.

Leontief, W. W. (1941): *The Structure of the American Economy, 1919–1939,* Oxford University Press, New York.

Leontief, W. W. (1953): *Studies in the Structure of the American Economy,* Oxford University Press, New York.

Leontief, W. W. (1961): "Lags and the Stability of Dynamic Systems," *Econometrica*, **29**, 659–69.

Madansky, A. (1964): "On the Efficiency of Three-Stage Least-Squares Estimation", *Econometrica*, **32**, 51–56.

Malinvaud, E. (1960): *Méthodes Statistiques de l' Économétrie*, Dunod, Paris.

Mann, H. B. and Wald, A. (1943): "On the Statistical Treatment of Linear Stochastic Difference Equations", *Econometrica*, **11**, 173–220.

Meade, J. E. (1960): *A Neo-Classical Theory of Economic Growth*, Allen and Unwin, London.

Morishima, M. (1960): "A Reconsideration of the Walras–Cassel–Leontief Model of General Equilibrium", Chapter 5 of *Mathematical Methods in the Social Sciences*, eds. K. J. Arrow, S. Karlin and P. Suppes, Stanford University Press.

Von Neumann, J. (1945, translated from German): "A Model of General Equilibrium" (G. Morgenstern tr.), *Review of Economic Studies*, **13**, 1–9.

Phelps, E. S. (1963): "Substitution, Fixed Proportions, Growth and Distribution", *International Economic Review*, **4**, 265–88.

Phillips, A. W. (1954): "Stabilization Policy in a Closed Economy", *Economic Journal*, **64**, 290–323.

Phillips, A. W. (1958): "The Relation between Unemployment and the Rate of Change in Money Wage Rates in the United Kingdom, 1861–1957", *Economica*, **25**, 283–99.

Phillips, A. W. (1959): "The Estimation of Parameters in Systems of Stochastic Differential Equations", *Biometrika*, **46**, 67–76.

Phillips, A. W. (1961): "A Simple Model of Employment Money and Prices in a Growing Economy", *Economica*, **28**, 360–70.

Redfern, P. (1955): "Net Investment in Fixed Assets in the United Kingdom, 1938–1953", *Journal of the Royal Statistical Society*, **A**, **118**, 141–92.

Rothenberg, T. J. and Leenders, C. T. (1964): "Efficient Estimation of Simultaneous Equation Systems", *Econometrica*, **32**, 57–76.

Samuelson, P. A. (1939): "Interactions between the Multiplier and the Principle of Acceleration", *Review of Economics and Statistics*, **21**, 75–8.

Samuelson, P. A. (1941): "The Stability of Equilibrium: Comparative Statics and Dynamics", *Econometrica*, **9**, 97–120.

Samuelson, P. A. (1948): *Foundations of Economic Analysis*, Harvard University Press.

Sargan, J. D. (1958): "The Instability of the Leontief Dynamic Model", *Econometrica*, **26**, 381–92.

Sargan, J. D. (1961): "Lags and the Stability of Dynamic Systems: A Reply", *Econometrica*, **29**, 670–3.

Sargan, J. D. (1964): "Three-Stage Least-Squares and Full Maximum-Likelihood Estimates", *Econometrica*, **32**, 77–81.

Solow, R. M. (1952): "The Structure of Linear Models", *Econometrica*, **20**, 29–46.

Solow, R. M. (1956): "A Contribution to the Theory of Economic Growth", *Quarterly Journal of Economics*, **70**, 65–94.

Solow, R. M. (1959): "Competitive Valuation in a Dynamic Input–Output System", *Econometrica*, **27**, 30–53.

Solow, R. M. (1960): "Investment and Technical Progress", Chapter 7 of *Mathematical Methods in the Social Sciences*, eds. K. J. Arrow, S. Karlin and P. Suppes, Stanford University Press.

Solow, R. M. (1963): "Heterogeneous Capital and Smooth Production Functions: An Experimental Study", *Econometrica*, **31**, 623–45.

Stone, J. R. N. (1954a): *Consumers' Expenditure and Behaviour in the United Kingdom, 1920–1938*, Cambridge University Press.

Stone, J. R. N. (1954b): "Linear Expenditure Systems and Demand Analysis: An Application to the Pattern of British Demand", *Economic Journal*, **64**, 511–27.

Struble, R. A. (1962): *Nonlinear Differential Equations*, McGraw-Hill, New York.

Swan, T. W. (1956): "Economic Growth and Capital Accumulation", *Economic Record*, **32**, 334–61.

Teigen, R. L. (1964): "Demand and Supply Functions for Money in the United States: Some Structural Estimates", *Econometrica*, **32**, 476–509.

Theil, H. (1953): "Estimation and Simultaneous Correlation in Complete Equation Systems", Centraal Planbureau, The Hague.

Theil, H. (1961): *Economic Forecasts and Policy*, second revised edition, North-Holland Publishing Co., Amsterdam.

Wald, A. (1951, translated from German): "On some Systems of Equations in Mathematical Economics". (O Eckstein tr.), *Econometrica*, **19**, 368–403.

Walras, L. (1954, translated from French): *Elements of Pure Economics* (W. Jaffé tr.), Allen and Unwin, London.

Wold, H. (1952): *Demand Analysis*, Almquist and Wicksell, Stockholm.

Zellner, A. and Theil, H. (1962): "Three-Stage Least-Squares: Simultaneous Estimation of Simultaneous Equations", *Econometrica*, **30**, 54–78.

INDEX

RENEWALS 458-4574
DATE DUE
FEB 16
GAYLORD
PRINTED IN U.S.A.